THE THING IS

The Thing Is

Christopher Potter

CONSTABLE

CONSTABLE

First published in Great Britain in 2020 by Constable

1 3 5 7 9 10 8 6 4 2

Copyright © Christopher Potter, 2020

Frontispiece: The unbroken seal on the door to the tomb of Tutankhamen.
Photographed by Harry Burton, 1922.
Reproduced with permission Griffith Institute, University of Oxford.

Illustrations by Naman Chaudhary

A CIP catalogue record for this book
is available from the British Library.

ISBN: 978-1-47213-434-9 (hardback)

Typeset in Caslon Pro by SX Composing DTP, Rayleigh, Essex
Printed and bound in Great Britain by Clays Ltd, Elcograf S.p.A.

Constable
An imprint of
Little, Brown Book Group
Carmelite House
50 Victoria Embankment
London EC4Y 0DZ

An Hachette UK Company
www.hachette.co.uk

www.littlebrown.co.uk

For Cy, Hazel and Sherry

In memory of my mother, Catherine Potter
(18 April 1934–16 January 2020)

These fragments I have shored against my ruins

I

FRAGMENTS

(i)   Everything not forbidden is compulsory.

(ii) Even Science, the strict measurer, is obliged to start with a make-believe unit.

(iii) Is gravity what it was, Willie, I fancy not.

(iv) I am one of those who are made for exceptions, not for laws.

COMMENTARY

Bang, bang, bang. Energy into particles. Bang bang bang. Particles into other particles. Stuff. Clouds of stuff. Gravity condensing stuff into stars and black holes. Stars and black holes arranged as galaxies, galaxies as clusters of galaxies, clusters of galaxies as clusters of clusters of galaxies. Bang, bang, bang. Galaxies colliding with other galaxies, stars colliding with other stars, planets and asteroids and comets banging into each other. Stars exploding. Bang, bang. Bang. Until eventually the clusters of clusters of galaxies, and the clusters of galaxies, and the galaxies and the stars and the planets all settle down, and everything settles down and stays in its own corner and there is hardly ever any banging any more. And now that that is out of the way and the universe is big enough and has enough stuff in it and all is quiet, now at last the time has arrived for something subtler to take place.

Not in the centre of a galaxy, not in a galaxy poor in metals, not in a globular galaxy, not near a source of gamma radiation, not in a multiple-star system nor even a binary-star system, not near a pulsar, not near stars that are too small, or stars that are too large, or near to a star that is about to turn into a supernova.

Not anywhere near a black hole, obviously; but on a planet in a steady orbit with a moon of the right size, not too hot, not too cold, with the right kind of volcanoes, and just the right amount of water, and the right combinations of various complex molecules, and just the right amount of time should have passed: three or four billion years should do it. Perhaps then.

Catascopos: the view from above, a godlike perspective.

In bed at night counting sheep. I've always wondered how this is meant to help. The sheep are all over the place. Instead, I try multiplying the number two by itself as many times as I can manage it: 2, 4, 8, 16, 32, 64, 128, 256, 512, 1024, 2048, 4096. Trickier now. 8192. Is that right? Can it be ninety-two when it was just ninety-six? Yes, seems so. 16394. Ninety-four this time. Surely something has gone wrong: 2, 4, 8, 16, 32 . . .

'The laws of physics,' he said, 'have conspired to make the collisions of atoms produce plants, kangaroos, insects and us.' You particularly enjoy the word 'conspire'.

One cell divides. Two cells. Two cells divide. Four cells. Eight cells. Sixteen, thirty-two . . . How many times to make a human being?

Once upon a time and far far away there lived a wise woman who had in her possession a book that contained all of the world's wisdom. Her name had long since been forgotten and she was known by the locals simply as The Oracle. Even though no one had ever seen inside the book – not that it would have made any difference as none of the locals could read – every one of them was immensely proud of the book, and the secret of its location was a closely guarded one. And yet somehow, over the years, as is the way of things, knowledge of the book's existence did find its way out into the wider world. A certain prince – his name does not matter – one day got to hear of the book, and as he was a prince of great learning he became determined to take possession of it, at any cost he said. It took years of journeying and a lot of good luck but eventually the prince found his way to The Oracle's cave, where she had lived as a hermit for many, many years now. The prince greeted her and stated his business. The Oracle said nothing by way of greeting, just named her price. The price was so high the prince was not even angry, he merely laughed and declined. The Oracle said nothing in reply, but tore the book in half and threw one of the halves into a fire that was burning beside her. The ancient, dried-up pages burned up in seconds as if they were autumn leaves. The prince was so taken aback he actually did take a step backwards. The Oracle held up the remaining pages and doubled her price. Now the prince really was angry, and once more declined. The Oracle ripped the half book in half again and again tossed one of the halves into the fire. Once more she doubled the price. By now the prince was beside himself with fury, but the kind of fury that comes from being wrong-footed. He was also frightened. So quickly did the bizarre negotiation proceed that soon the book that contained all of the world's wisdom had been reduced to a few fragments and the asking price was now all the wealth the prince possessed. If this were a fairy story the prince would at this point have agreed to The Oracle's price and we would be left wondering at the story's moral. As it was, the prince returned home, defeated, and none the wiser.

Perhaps the universe began a step at a time, like a particle of dust stepping, dancing on the surface of a pond:

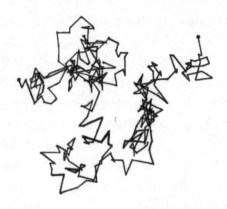

Or perhaps the universe comes into existence gesturally, as if by the waving of a wand? Like this perhaps, like the pattern traced out by Uncle Toby's stick:

By gradual scale sublimed (or whatever) somehow the universe turned soul into body, or was it vice versa?

Or at 9 a.m. on 23 October 4004 BC. And what day of the week would that have been? A civilised hour for sure, but quite late in England for first light.

Enantiodromia: the tendency of something to change into its opposite.

Somewhere, you read that the novelist William Golding 'held reality in scorn'.

What is it that integrates the world of countable things? Which is the illusion, the apparent discreteness or the apparent continuity of the world? It is important to you that you have it both ways, though you are not entirely sure why. Perhaps it is why you are so drawn to cosmology. What could be more discrete, more of a one-off, than the Big Bang? What could be more on-going – perhaps not everlasting, but near enough for your purposes – than the expansion of the universe?

Or perhaps the most possible of all possible worlds.

Shove anything problematical over there. Yes, right over there, right back to the beginning. Yes, keep on going. Further, further back. Back to the beginning of everything. If you wish to make an apple pie from scratch, said the cosmologist, first you must invent the universe. That's better. Reduce, reduce. Simplifications must be made. There are those first particles, and there is what those particles afterwards became. Should be enough for anyone. O Primal Energy, I worship thee. I believe in the one universe, the universe all mighty. The origins of the universe traced back to something singular. Once upon a time. In the beginning was the Word. Back to the Big Bang, or to Adam, or to some other arbitrary point from which, supposedly, everything followed.

There are considerations to be made, of course. There always are.

She was not a scientist, but she had good instincts. Once, after someone had laboriously described to her the differences between Newton's and Einstein's theories of gravity – a kind of attraction, said Newton; the path of least resistance, an illusion of attraction, said Einstein – she smiled slyly in reply, and observed that it seemed to her that gravity was physics' first pass at a theory of love. Not bad for a first attempt, but things have moved on, she said. Don't you just adore the old cosmologies. Modern science all very well if what interests you is averages. Plato and the demiurge. A cosmos with an aim, not just an accounting for possible endings. The aim is goodness, Plato said. Modern cosmology all very well too, but where is the Henry James in all this? Human beings the flotsam and jetsam of the universe. Fine I suppose. What is jetsam? Skip the detail where life is. Skip over Henry James. Skip over everything. Everything that matters to me. Hands up who has read the *Principia*? If not Newton, someone else itching to get at gravity. The aristocracy of art. Problematic. How many for a Mozart? Dead at what? Thirty-four, was it? Notebook mapped out into a future that never came. And there was biology, she said. Had another go at it. Altruism. Getting warmer. Still, things move on, always move on, and now here we are.

Over dinner a friend casually remarks that once, when he was five, he saw an angel. You are too polite to enquire further. Another opportunity lost.

And now you wonder if you have been asking the wrong questions. Perhaps the flow of the world just is, and it is the countable world that must be accounted for.

And never was there such a dinner since the world began. Now that's what any cosmology worth its salt ought to be able to accommodate.

He said that the only events of significance in the universe were the Big Bang and the Apocalypse. I mean really, what do you say to people like that?

I saw Francis Bacon once, in the flesh, High Street Kensington Station, late afternoon, standing on the opposite platform, bulging plastic carrier bags in each hand. No one else recognised him; or if they did, like me they weren't letting on. There had been this small coincidence of time and space in which forever after I could say that I had once seen Francis Bacon, standing on the platform opposite, bulging carrier bags in each hand.

If you can't measure it, it doesn't exist, your tutor once said to you. You thought about it and set off on an entirely different course.

The plucky bubble-that-could expanded out of nothingness and kept on going.

Plot any seven points of transcendence since the Big Bang along axis t (time). Estimate how long until the next one. You may have a billion years either way. (Use Greenwich Mean Time.)

Must be life elsewhere. A miracle otherwise. Can't have that. Not to be countenanced. Got to get out of this one. Try this. Millions of other planets, billions probably. Must be life. Here, so must be there. *No better than gambling. So many losses must be a hit next time. Should know better. Numbers too large. Too unstable. Too many variables. Can't be proved. Undecidable.* Can't admit that, don't believe it. OK, if you really insist, willing to accept that it is possible – if highly, highly unlikely. Have you written that down? Let's call it the *visible* universe. A local shop for local people. Universe downgrade. Just one of many. 10^{80}, is it? There, get out of that one. *And yet here we are. Not miracle enough for you?*

What a lovely metaphor, she said. In order to make room for what that first stuff afterwards became, what else could the universe do but expand? I can perfectly understand, she said, why you would want to save love for another day.

The dismal idea that everything is laid out, like some singular immovable object: everything that has happened and everything that will happen screwed down and fixed in place. You prefer instead to believe that every moment of existence offers a chance to witness something new in the world, something evanescent, something – for being made once only – miraculous.

You were seated at dinner next to a philosopher you had long admired. You were eager to talk about the nausea of first causes. He wanted to talk to his attractive neighbour seated on his other side about pretty much anything else. You persisted. Finally, he told you that for him the First Cause was a non-problem, that for him the Big Bang and the vacuum were enough. You were disappointed, shocked really, did not know what to say. There was nothing else to say. You thought, I have often seen you at the opera. I thought you were one of us.

Greetings, aliens! Have you discovered the scientific method? Let's compare notes. Ah, I see you took a different course.

II

FRAGMENTS

Am I telling the story, or is the story telling me?

COMMENTARY

Once upon a time, far far away in a remote quadrant of the universe, in a world so like this world that you might hardly be aware of the differences, three astronauts are preparing for blast off: a poet, a philosopher and a priest.

You remember it as though it were yesterday, the day it had been announced that the universe had had a beginning in time. Around the world everyone was talking about it. All night celebrations. Palpable relief. The masses embraced mass, crazy for heft. The vogue was for fat. People planted their feet more firmly on the ground, walked then with heavier steps. The Big Bang! It makes you smile to think how quickly everyone embraced the singularity. For years afterwards people would say, where were you on that day? I knew it, I knew it all along your friends said to you: I knew the universe must have begun in time, just as the Bible says. But they hadn't. No one had.

To be at one with your machine as you were. To be machine and let go of the ego. A machine among machines only. Flesh as machine. Universe as machine.

Here was where I found myself, one of my kind, with no memory of what I was and no knowledge of what, by being here, I had become.

The rocket was barely a machine at all, closer to an invocation, something like abracadabra, something still physical but scarcely so, a something almost ineffable.

When I first saw the planet, you were so far away everything looked the same. From far enough away, everything always looks the same.

Particles. I thought you looked like particles. What I might have done to you!

How long have I been watching? I still don't know how to answer that question. Where I came from was in a state of fervency, that much I remember. I had to learn to trade desire for energy. I had to learn to accept the pretence of the particle. I felt the loss.

I had to start from scratch. Every step closer closed off the way back to what I had been before. Words. Things. Words attached to things. Time passing. Only then did I begin to see the differences. A physical perspective has changed everything. I don't know how I got here.

I look and I read. Novels mostly. How many orbits is it now? They told me that I had to wait, but I forget who. They told me that you are not ready yet. And so I have waited. I do not intervene. Occasionally, in small ways, out of boredom. And now, after all this time, I have come to the conclusion that it is too late anyway, and that perhaps it had always been too late.

Once upon a time I was somewhere else. I must have been.

III

FRAGMENTS

(i) *I think it's better to be born. At least you know where you are.*

(ii) *But it had all happened before, of course. Everything has always happened before. Except to children.*

COMMENTARY

Somehow you had to learn how to make yourself fit. And you did not fit.

As a child you wanted to be a robot; not one of those domestic robots that do jobs around the house, you were that already; you wanted to escape the prison of being a child, but not into the prison of being an adult; you wanted to live without emotions: not a child and not an adult, not a human being at all.

There's something definite about being a robot. As a child you felt as if you were ill-defined, ungrounded. You felt as if you had been incompletely translated from wherever, whatever it was that you had been before.

You knew you were a changeling child, until that day of disappointment arrived when you looked into the mirror and what you saw reflected there was the unmistakable expression of your family's genes.

New story. If not a changeling perhaps an alien that has chosen to look as if it belongs to this family, a necessary part of the plan of not being found out.

You longed to run away, as children do; packed and stowed away a bag, jam sandwiches for the journey, ready to make a midnight flit, only to miss the appointed hour felled by sleep.

He said, The human being is the most precise physical machine that can exist. So which is elevated, she asked: the machine or human beings?

There were days you'd wake up feeling intoxicated with desire. You stood on your head so that the world might stand on its head, somersaulted so that the world might somersault. You jumped in the air, jumped off the garden shed, jumped from as high up the staircase as you dared. You jumped that you might jump out of the world. You jumped for joy.

You were always interested in the details: the details without which your machine would not have got you here, and of course – though it took you a long time of looking – in the details that make you what you are.

There are nights your sleeping body heads straight to the forest, not further in but further down, a route all too familiar.

How wonderful the electrical impulses in the brain seen illuminated on the screen like star maps. How wonderful to see, so near at hand, the effects of the something ineffable that is a thought, now translated into the physical world; the something that happens between thought and action! Do I dare say transubstantiated? Here you come, right up to the precipice. You stand at the cliff edge, at your back all of the physical world massing in your support. You step forward. You step easily across the worlds of the mental and the physical. The step is a leap. The leap is accomplished, but you do not know across what you are leaping, and you do not how you made the leap, and you do not know what is in the chasm across which you have leaped. Of what consequence the physical world now?

The small door in the tree through which she can only just force her way, leads by a narrow corridor to a flight of narrow stairs. The staircase gradually widens. The faint glow from the door by which she entered gradually fades. Now a faint glow ahead gradually increases in brightness. As she descends, the steps become more solid, earth to stone. In the growing light she can see now that the stairs are made of marble and are increasing in size with every step she takes. And then all of a sudden there are no more stairs and she finds herself looking out into a vast cavern.

Pantophobia: a morbid fear of everything.

There's nothing out there to be afraid of, your parents said to you one night, meaning to be comforting. You spent all night lying there, thinking of the nothing that might be coming to get you.

Another night, a different tack. It occurred to you that the real terror is not the terror of the void, of nothingness, but the terror of existence: that there is anything at all, the sheer impossibility of it. And even that, the impossibility of it, impossible too. Clearly there is nothing at all, and yet I exist. How can that be? How could it all have begun? You wondered if perhaps your own recent coming into existence was a kind of dream. You were not comforted by the thought.

You made a time machine. You put the things in the box and buried it. You waited.

The history teacher ordered the class to be silent for five minutes. Not a sound. After three or four intolerable minutes a boy she liked very much accidentally dropped something on the floor. The sight of him trying to retrieve what bounced here and there and continually escaped his grasp, the silent pantomime of expressions that crossed his face was too much for her. Her fear was overwhelmed by something else, something like love, perhaps joy. And so, though she was a timid and obedient child, the laughter exploded out of her. She was soon convulsed with laughing, the laughter feeding off its own energy. The entire class began to join in, and to her relief so did the teacher, which made everyone laugh the more.

Describe a room, or perhaps it is a long corridor, severe and classical, lined with antique heads, no, a library, a grand library. There are mahogany shelves, good rugs, tables and lights, many lights, casting many shadows, there are clocks, you see the pendulums swinging, but as intently as you listen you hear nothing, and among the shadows as you move a sense grows in you that you are moving outside time.

You do not know what you are. Sometimes you think, no more than a machine. Other times you think, what a machine!

You did not know then what you know now: that what you wished to flee was your existence. You know that you will escape in the end. Just a matter of sitting it out.

IV

FRAGMENTS

(i) *He told me how to know a dog otter's spoor from a gravid bitch's.*

(ii) *Spent the day measuring the legs and antennae of lice to two decimal places.*

(iii) Homo artifex, homo faber, homo Fabergé.

(iv) *I read, and sigh, and wish I were a tree.*

(v) *A big part of the woolly mammoth's diet was made up of tiny flowers.*

COMMENTARY

The birds, dreaming of when they were dinosaurs, stare at the cats, and the cats stare back.

Once, when you were huddled deep in the cave, you knew that, in the dark, one or two of you would be picked off in the night; one or two fewer of you by daylight. Now, sometimes, the cats scratch or bite you, but mostly they purr, seduce rather than destroy, the only power of mastery left to them.

As a child you were obsessed with hiding. You were not very good at it. You thought you could make yourself disappear just by shutting your eyes. You were, however – like all children – acutely sensitive to whatever you suspected was being hidden from you. When you heard an adult conversation cut short, your antenna was at its most sensitive. You knew something was being withheld from you. In the hope that the missing details might be filled in later, you stored away what you had managed to glean. Years later you heard the one thing that finally made sense of what you had not fully understood at the time, as if the answer had always been out there waiting for you.

I knew what to keep quiet about.

The deer falls exhausted knowing that you are on its trail, even if miles behind. But you have mastered the signs: hoof prints and spoors, broken twigs, tufts of hair, scents in the air. Look. Listen. You have modelled your world in signs.

Spatilomancy: divination by studying animal excrement. Myomancy: divination by studying the movement of mice. Caliology: the study of birds' nests. Haruspex: an official who predicts the future by inspecting the entrails of sacrificial animals.

Every day of the mammoth's life is recorded in dentine. So says the expert in mammoth tusks.

Even if it were us who killed them off, all those missing hominids, lonelier without them.

Consider: to look at with attention, from *con sidere*, with the stars, perhaps originally a term of augury.

What is there when the light isn't? Nothing. The light falling on the thing gives the thing its thingness. Leonardo knew.

Signals sent along neural pathways flowing from your brain, down your spine, radiating out across your body into the world. Signals collected from the world and sent along those same neural pathways back to your brain.

The world may be an illusion, but even illusions exist; something has to if the trick is to make its effect.

It has to be seen to be believed, and not always even then.

Seeing and just as importantly being seen, two of the main drivers of evolution. Size for size the human retina is the most energetic part of your body, consumes even more oxygen than your brain.

Light hits your retina and energy from the photons causes certain molecules to turn through 180 degrees, the beginning of the process of seeing. The energy transferred from the photons has to be just the right amount, only those photons from the part of the electromagnetic spectrum called visible light, otherwise too much energy, or too little.

Potassium and sodium molecules drift across cells. Voltages build up. Ion gates open. Synapses fire.

The eye turns to the unexpected object even before the conscious brain has named it for the benefit of the ego. The ego comprehends and returns a feeling response back to the body.

Looking requires a degree of effort, concentration, directedness. Most of you, most of the time, look minimally. None of you looks with as much attention as you might. To varying degrees, the world passes you by.

You do not see yourself. You are always giving yourself away, for the simple reason that you look out at the world, not back on yourself. You have almost no idea what you look like. About yourself you miss almost everything. You cannot get outside of yourself. You do not even know how many outsides there are.

You had wondered what your planet might look like seen from the outside. Persistence got you there in the end.

You look out at other people and become good at reading the tics and signs, the minute clues that tell you what the others do not know even about themselves.

You try to read her face. You are looking for emotional cues and information. You are looking for the verb that makes sense of the sentence.

A rare disease: she has lost the ability to make sense even of the faces of those she knows best and loves most dearly. She is overwhelmed and distressed at her failure. She sees that he looks exactly like her lover, yet she feels nothing. That he no longer elicits any emotional response in her tells her that it cannot really be him. Has an alien adopted his form? Is the person in front of her a robot? She knows that that is ridiculous, but she has run out of alternative narratives. What has become of her lover? When the zombie speaks, her distress becomes even greater. She recognises the voice, but where is he?

Do you not know what a good listener you are? How droll? How handsome in that suit? How kind? Do you know how charming you are? That disarming walk of yours, bolt upright, your arms down by your side. That glance, that way you have of holding your head when your mind is elsewhere. You have no idea what effect you make when you enter a room. You have no idea what effect you have on me when you enter a room. You come in stealthily and you think that no one sees. But I see. Your shoulders lift slightly, your head drops slightly; you look up from your long hair, a quick glance, the hint of a smile. Even your brain. Such interesting firing patterns going on in there. I see the invisible traces you trail behind and in front of you. You do not know that I am near. You do not know that I love you.

Did you see that? said the photographer; the way the light changed, just for a moment. But you hadn't, of course.

When the Hubble telescope was properly polished, the universe became clearer by hundreds of billions of stars.

For a time, a painting by the French artist David was lauded as being close to perfection. And then, one day, the experts took another look. The painting was not by David they now said. It was painted by some minor artist, a woman. The painting was moved to the basement.

Those who had been at the first atom-bomb tests said afterwards that they hadn't known that there would be so much light. They said that for a moment the entire world around them looked more real.

Aged seven or eight, Darwin fell from a footpath that ran atop an old fortification in Shrewsbury. Of the moment of falling he wrote afterwards that the number of thoughts which passed through his mind was astonishing. Even then, not only paying attention but paying attention to paying attention.

Woven DNA. A genie in a bottle. Word made flesh.

Whatever kind of machine you are, even the machine is ghostly, an illusion. Ghosts of ghosts then.

Tosca is singing, but today what you hear is the bassoon supporting her. Today it is as if Puccini wants you to hear that bassoon.

V

FRAGMENTS

(i)   *I feel more and more every day, as my imagination strengthens, that I do not live in the world alone but in a thousand worlds.*

(ii)   *Where what cannot be seen is inferred by what the visible does.*

(iii)   *We have all got to exert ourselves a little to keep sane, and call things by the same names as other people call them by.*

(iv)   *We are more important than our present selves.*

(v)   *The ego is not master in its own house.*

(vi)   *Who am I indeed? Perhaps a personage in disguise.*

(vii)   *It is easier for us to notice our own deficiencies when they become observable in others.*

COMMENTARY

Remember long ago when you were apes and there were so many different kinds of you? And if you cast your mind really far back, remember when you were fish, and before that worms? Remember when you were bacteria? Remember the Big Bang? It was so long ago you have forgotten much of the detail. After so long the details get lost. Though now you come to think of it, you are not sure that in those early days there was that much detail anyway. Your options then were severely limited.

Evolution has always made do with what is at hand. In the beginning there was only the one stuff. Our options have never been so limited as they were then. Every season in the aeons since, the universe offers up new products, more various and more sophisticated, and in addition to what was on offer last season. Sometimes lines are withdrawn. After fourteen billion years there is plenty to choose from. Not quite Liberty Hall: the range of choices is wide, but it is a range nevertheless.

All complex life is basically yeast organised differently. So which should we be in awe of: yeast, or the power of organisation?

Every recombination of human DNA another attempt to make a person more beautiful, wiser, kinder than anyone who has come before. The downside: more maleficent, crueller, dumber. Every newborn holds the promise of the entire human experiment, and hence, of course, because it is the fate of all newborns to grow up, so does every human being. The tragedy is that none will fulfil the promise held out for the human race. Every adult is inevitably destined to disappoint. And so attention is expectantly turned back to the children.

Kindness: being of a kind.

When I first joined the company, I asked if I might buy my own office furniture. The request was turned down. What would they do with the furniture if I left? Instead, I was sent a brochure from which I might make my choices and an email that read: your options are severely limited.

She remembers her father saying to the visiting vicar, his first visit to their house, soon after they had moved in, that the boulders in their garden, he had been told, were particularly old. In her memory, the vicar is half the age her father is, but she does the maths and she realises with a shock that her father was half the age that she is now, and that the vicar, young as he was, can't have been more than ten years younger than her father, though ten years when you are eleven years old, as she then was, is a lifetime. The vicar said, but aren't all rocks old? Her father laughed and said that he supposed that that must be true. She felt for him. She saw that it wasn't about the words themselves, or whether or not her father had uttered some solecism, but that an opportunity to exert power had been taken, and an opportunity to be kind let slip. What hurt, and hurts even now, is that her father had wanted to say something conversational – she knew it had cost him greatly to be this social – and his attempt had been quashed. He had invited the vicar in, and the vicar had chosen to make the world smaller. Worse – she now knows – her father had not been wrong. Of course all rocks are old, but there are rocks that are older than other rocks, much older. She saw then and sees it still, that her father was the better man, but she remembers, too, that she turned to look at the handsome, worldly young vicar and found herself attracted to him.

At the Ryedale show in North Yorkshire one of the prizes is for best sponge cake. Every cake is to be made according to the exact same recipe. Each of the twenty or so cakes looks quite different one from the other.

With my looks and your brains how could we fail, Isadora Duncan said to George Bernard Shaw. But what if our children were to have my looks and your brains, Shaw said in reply. You used to love this kind of thing. Now it just makes you uncomfortable. And not just the misogyny. A fondness still, however. A memory of who you had once been and a time there was.

At Burton Constable Hall, near Skirlaugh in East Yorkshire, where William Constable put together what was said to have been one of the best *Wunderkammer* in all of Europe. A keen amateur scientist, he tried to cross rabbits and hens, but they all came out looking like hens.

She feared that what she was and what she had become defined her, had turned her into a cliché. Who wants to be explained away? She says to herself, Why should my genes have the last word? I am not glad to be the way I am any more than I am glad that I exist. As a girl she had wanted to be different only on her own terms. She believed then that she was a free agent in the world, if only she could work out how to act in the world. She knew she was clever, which was difference of a kind, but not difference enough. For a time she wanted to believe that she was unlike anyone who had ever lived before. When she was a young woman she thought she saw in Christ the exceptionalism she was looking for. She thought he personified true free will. She thought that it was because of how he had lived that he became what he afterwards became. At some point she discovered that what she believed was an ancient heresy. The discovery made her feel nauseous. She can reconjure that feeling even now. She was sure the world had made a terrible mistake and that it was too late ever to put right the wrong. If she had lived then she would have been burned at the stake, assuming, that is, that anyone would have noticed her enough to care, or that she had been educated enough to have been able to express her beliefs, or assuming that she had had any freedom to have had taken away from her.

She continued to go to church, for a while anyway: for the words, the music and the ritual. She knew she no longer believed what was being spouted there. She came to despise all organised religion.

As she grew older, as the number of options available to her grew more and more limited, she saw, with relief, that not only was she not exceptional, but that she was just like everyone else.

From his prison cell, the Republican Aubrey Harrington – 'a gentleman of high spirit and a hot head' – took a fancy that his perspiration was turning into flies 'and sometimes to bees'. You particularly like that detail. And sometimes to bees. Adds veracity. We are good at that, making our stories sound like the truth, whatever that is.

The inattentive young man does not see that he is walking toward the edge of a deep hole, does not see the approaching rabid dog, fails to notice the banana skin. The incompetent multitasker tapping on her phone and crossing the road fails to accomplish both tasks and is run down and killed by the aged, inattentive driver. The aged driver though past his sexual potency continues to alter the gene pool so long as he holds on to his licence.

Life yearns to exist and is profligate. Imagine how strong the yearning in the early days.

Striated and smooth muscle evolved separately.

Everything wants to find not victory over other things, but its own place in the scheme of things. Everything wants to find the place where it fits best, and the place that is itself the best fit. If that means pushing others out of the way then so be it, but the pushing is incidental; the intent is to be at home.

The behaviourists say that love is merely an inducement to propagate genes. Keats said that he could not live without the love of his friends, and meant it.

Do you remember when you used to say that animals have no feelings, that they are merely automata? You used to say that birds have no sense of smell, taste or touch. Today you say that some echolocate, some see UV radiation, some sense the Earth's magnetic field. Do you remember when you used to say that flies cannot be taught anything? And then you looked more closely. Now you say you can teach a fly all kinds of things. You have been looking closely for a hundred years and still they take you by surprise.

You say you can't teach an old dog new tricks.

You say a lot of things.

Except for those you arbitrarily assigned as pets, you had not thought of animals as individuals. For you each species had existed as one creature repeated over and over again, which, funnily enough, was how I first saw you too: just the one of you repeated over and over again.

Ungrounded in my spaceship, I am always tearful. Which is it I fear more: being inside or being outside? Claustrophobia or agoraphobia?

Outside is almost everything; inside, that strange state of being alive which is no one thing but a set of relationships; perhaps not even a set, which suggests something countable, discrete and thing-like, but a process of investigation.

As you swim, warm-blooded in the cold sea, you feel the pull of the cold-blooded fish. You feel the heat being drawn out of you. A swift, cold death it would be.

A man runs along the shoreline shouting, but he is too far away. You do not know what he is shouting about, but you are compelled by his urgency and heave yourself out of the heavy ocean. You are thinking only crowd thoughts. Along the beach, strings of you come ashore like strands of wilful seaweed.

You see two strata of fish, a stratum of pursuers and a stratum of the pursued. A feeding frenzy. The ocean boiling cold. Silver fish chased to the margins make silvery suicidal leaps and cascade onto the sandy shore, where you lie gasping and hot and they twitch in cold silvery death throes. You cannot count how many.

I have not been myself.

Must be several Mozarts here somewhere. But where? They are living in the excrement of capitalism and imperialism's slums, a friend says to you. She's paraphrasing William James, she says. You wonder if the days of Mozart, like the star-making days and the days of miracles, are simply over and done with. It was a once-in-a-universe opportunity. The window narrowed and closed up.

I said I had had the best meal I could ever remember eating, but when he asked me what I had eaten, I couldn't remember anything about the meal at all. All I could remember was the feeling I had had. I can't believe you can say you had one of the best meals you have ever had but can't tell me anything about it, he said. I said nothing, knew then that I would probably not see him again.

She had watched and waited and listened. She had kept her secrets to herself and so had become, though she did not know it, and because she kept the secrets for so long, a secret to herself.

You exist only because of the others. You are all in this together. If it weren't for them you would wake up not knowing who it was that you had been the day before. You would be intolerably lonely if it were not for the others. And I don't just mean family and friends; I mean everyone who has ever crossed your path. And I don't just mean everyone; I mean every bird that you have ever encountered or has ever encountered you, every plant. You are the integral of everyone you have ever met, of everything you have ever seen or read, every conversation, every shared meal, indeed everyone who has ever lived and everything that has ever existed. It is not possible to be alone in the world. If you were truly alone you would be nothing at all. You only mean something in relation to other people and other things, just as motion would be meaningless if there was only the one thing in the universe. If your life were not contingent it would be nothing. Not alone, but whether or not you are lonely is another matter altogether.

VI

FRAGMENTS

I long ago lost a hound, a bay horse and a turtle dove, and am still on their trail.

COMMENTARY

How she negotiated the cat flap, gingerly tapping the door with her paw and then all of a sudden rushing through; how, when I was sitting by the window, she would sit on the window ledge and miaow from the outside even though the door right next to the window was open; how she would be one moment entirely sedentary and serious seeming and then suddenly decide to run after a leaf; the disdain she felt for her brother and all other cats; how she would run away if anyone came to the door; how eventually she became curious about our friends when they visited but never when it was a workman; how she slept on my shoulder; how, when I turned in the night, I had to turn slowly under her so that she, like a circus dog on a ball, was left undisturbed, coming to rest finally on my other shoulder; how she loved ice cream; how she hated the smell of oranges; the way she would behave badly as if entirely for our entertainment, jumping onto the table while we were eating; how she loved the melted butter left on a plate after we had had crumpets; how in old age she achieved self-consciousness, one day recognising herself in a mirror when she never had done before; how she grew accustomed to fireworks; how she would suddenly dash up and down the stairs for no reason; how refined she was, never eating more than the tiniest mouthful of food at a time; how aged eighteen she appeared to be dying and would no longer eat or drink; how the vet kept her hydrated for a week or so but then said it was now up to her; how when she came back home she immediately started to eat and drink again and lived for another two years; how she would eat the same food day after day and then suddenly refuse to eat it ever again; how she would sulk when we were packing our bags and about to go on a trip; how she would sulk when we came back again; how eventually she forgave us; how in her last years she gave up sulking; how when I put my hand out on top of the duvet she would winch herself down on it, purring; how she would suddenly be in my lap and I had no recollection of how she had got there; how she rejected nearly all the toys we bought her, that what she enjoyed best was to chase after a piece of string dragged along the floor; how she would lift one paw, like a lion rampant; how one day she suddenly learned how to miaow, at first a small cracked sound, but later as loud as the sound of a screaming baby; how she would sit at the bottom of the stairs at first light yowling; how I would have to get up and throw my slippers at her in an effort to get her to stop; how she would stop for a few minutes and then start up again; how I would in the end have to get up and bring her up to bed, hold her down next to me while I tried to get back to sleep; how she would come and wake me up by rubbing her face into my face; how when she was older she would shake her head and thin liquid would spray from her mouth and nostrils sometimes finding its way into my eyes; her range of facial expressions she wore like masks: angry, adoring, loving, disdainful; how some days she was affectionate and then the next day aloof; how sometimes she could become very clingy; how she had to sit on any papers I was working on; her vague attempts to catch birds; the day she caught a pigeon, or more likely came across a dead one, and brought it up to the bed purring madly; how when she ate grass we knew a furball would not be far behind; how thin she was when we first inherited her from the previous owners of the house; how her previous owners had moved only two streets away; how she would repeatedly return to her old house; how her old owners finally asked if we might adopt her; how we had hoped that they would ask; how gracefully she leapt from roof to roof; her constant grooming; her snow-white chest and paws; how thin she was at the end and how bald; how she was always there to greet us as if she had been waiting all the time we were out; how sometimes we would creep up to the front door when we returned home hoping to surprise her; how we'd slowly open the letterbox as quietly as we possibly could, but there she'd be sitting on the mat, waiting; how occasionally we'd see her coming down the stairs just as we were coming in through the gate; how she loved to be rubbed under the chin; how she hated to be combed but loved the result; how we worried that she wouldn't settle into her and our new home because she had only ever lived in the one place; the way she immediately loved the new house, because it was grander we decided; how she lapped just the tiniest amount of milk at a time; how in her last days she would stagger into the garden, head for the pond and fall straight in; the look she gave me when we had to take her to the vet for the final time; how when we tried to bury her in the garden I couldn't bring myself to throw the soil directly onto her body and had to get a tea towel to place over her; how all these years later we miss her still.

VII

FRAGMENTS

(i)   *At a few places on the planet there are trapdoors to infinity.*

(ii) *Those thoughts that wander through Eternity.*

(iii) *I also wanted to know more about how they felt being away from their planet, whether anything changed – perspective, dreams, language even. I mean, do you still get up in the morning when there's no such thing as up? Is there even such a thing as morning?*

COMMENTARY

She embroiders, in her palace waiting. Time weighs on her heavily. An hour might as well be eternity. Every day she looks out of the window and wonders if it will be today. Year after year passes, but still he does not return.

A calf's heart, still beating. To the dead body priests bring the energy of the living. Inside a solid-gold catafalque the linen-wrapped body is covered in an outer layer of papyrus inscribed with spells. Inside the wrappings the mummified body is gestating, ready to be reborn into the afterlife. The sarcophagus is not a coffin, it is a cocoon.

Thousands of years before they were rediscovered, someone had been the last person to leave the caves. Someone left the last footprint before the land slipped and blocked the entrance chamber seemingly forever. No winds, no animals, nothing and no one entered the cave again. The years passed, decades, centuries, millennia. The footprints in the dust lay unchanged.

I look out across the ocean, vast and empty and imagine some creature rising out of the waters, a creature so large it stretches, as the ocean does, from horizon to horizon. I imagine the creature rising out of the water to stand miles high.

Approaching the moon I see only empty space. I know that it is the moon itself that is blocking out the stars, but the experience is of a sky suddenly and completely emptied of everything. One day, in deep time, this is how the night sky will look. Gradually, one by one, stars will move beyond the edge of the horizon of the visible universe. From whatever vantage point, the night sky will be completely empty.

What I see is mostly radiation, dotted here and there the odd hundreds of billions of stars. Seen one part of the electromagnetic spectrum, seen it all; seen one star, seen a hundred billion.

For as long as no one looks at her, the princess escapes quantum entanglement and exists outside of time. Until, one day, a prince turns up and opens the door to the room in which she lies. The quantum wave collapses, and the princess disappears, not even in a cloud of smoke.

Meet me at the threshold, my father used to say. I have always loved that word, makes me think of winding mossy ways, underground passages, undiscovered tombs, secret lakes under the earth where blind white fish slither enormous and silently past each other through thick, oily waters.

A black-and-white photograph of the door to an ancient Egyptian tomb taken a century ago and moments before the rope is cut, the seal broken, the bolt drawn back, and the tomb re-entered.

Three thousand years earlier, they had sealed the door and turned away, only to find themselves lost in corridors of time. And now here they are again, once more at the threshold, back where they started from, dazed as if from a dream. Nothing has changed.

Abracadabra
Open sesame
Words that open doors
Doors within doors
Doors disguised to look like something else: shelves of books, or part of a tapestry for instance
Doors that lead to ways of escape
Doors that lead from darkened rooms suddenly to the middle of a day outdoors. Strange construction. Outdoors. As if the door itself is the key to the world, the door itself that expels us into the world.

The boy at school who hanged himself on the back of the cellar door, feet dangling over the precipitous cellar steps; an experiment that had gone wrong, they said; but how did they know? A common occurrence, they said; the young flirting with death.

Civilisation collapsed and no one walked on the moon again. Footprints there unchanged and unseen. Now, ten thousand years later, a thirteenth human being. The old footprints as fresh as the new ones, exactly as they were when they were first imprinted those few years, long long ago.

Aeons pass. Occasionally a meteorite thumps noiselessly to the ground nearby.

She is rarely in the present. She is almost always somewhere else: sometimes in thoughts that push her into the past or into the future, mostly somewhere else altogether that takes her outside time and space. And yet she is continually flicked momentarily into the present by life going on around her. Taken up by her thoughts the real world disappears. The cup of tea is no longer by her side, the room, the chair in which she is sitting, everything disappears, even her own self, all of it vanishes, until she twitches back with a start into time, into her body, into the room and into an external world consistent with the world as it had been before she left it. She keeps coming back into the world only to leave it once more.

There is something already nostalgic about the photograph that was taken of you just yesterday.

Like walking through the dusty halls of a marble palace from which the inhabitants have long since departed. Time slowed down. Nothing changes here. Sky a velvet cloth on which an uncountable number of diamonds have been thrown down. Brilliant-cut sharp shadows. The sense of not being anywhere. Shades of grey. Not alive but not quite dead either. Sometimes a hint of silver, sometimes gold. For long ages I was amazed at the beauty of this place. Now I would do anything to see a tree. I miss trees as much as I miss people. If I could, I might trade my life for a few more moments in the company of birds. That I might hear a bird sing again is almost too much to hope for, the desire too much to bear.

Falling through time and finding yourself in eternity.

When astronauts began to orbit the Earth for the first time, they saw the sun rise and the sun set every ninety minutes.

Round and around, sunrise and sunset over and over again. And above the atmosphere, seen from space, they became aware that every sunrise was exactly the same as every other sunrise, every sunset like every other sunset, and that until now there had been no one to see it, and no one to say: every day for billions of years the sun has risen and has set in exactly the same way, the sky spectacularly running the gamut of the rainbow.

It is an early Renaissance painting, the life and martyrdom of some obscure young saint. You can't be bothered to read the label and find out who. Are those, what look like callipers, the symbol of his martyrdom? Or that hammer? Those nails? His life story is depicted as a succession of images. You think, The painter has found a way of adding time into the painting as another dimension, inextricable from space but of some other nature. You think then of that painting by Holbein in which an ectoplasmic something can only be resolved if the painting is squinted at obliquely from one side. A skull it turns out. You think, The painter has attempted to add an extra dimension of space to his painting, or perhaps not so much a dimension of space as a threshold.

But there were no sunrises, no sunsets. Not really. There only appeared to be because a human being was in motion around the Earth.

You know yourself well enough to know that if you were ever to slip the bounds of yourself completely you would be utterly annihilated and that there would not be any way back.

The city buried beneath this city: mosaic floors, pots and porticos, statues whole and fragmented, the lost dead, all the stuff of ages gone by jumbled and broken and covered up, sinking slowly in processes of slow and steady accretion, and then sometimes suddenly and seismically wrenched further underground.

That's me there, he said, pointing at a photograph of the Big Bang.

Why would a poet have been any better at describing the experience of walking on another celestial body? Your poets are not good at describing experiences to order. They have trodden on other planets already. The moon is not a door, one of them once wrote. This is the light of the mind, wrote another, blue and planetary.

Sometimes, out there, I get the feeling that all of space is filled up with some vast otherness, as if the emptiness itself were unstable, as if only a veil, easily torn, separates us from some other reality.

I had been weightless for so long, that when I returned I'd lean too far forward, lose my balance and fall over. The moon was a more forgiving place. Some said bleak and boring. Not to me. True, the landscape is empty and unrelenting, an unvarying scene of boulders, ravines and arid mountains. True, there is no atmosphere to soften the light, which gives the massive jagged mountains a threatening quality, but there is something intimate about this place too. The mountains are like two-dimensional cut-outs, as if part of some restrained stage design. At certain times, when the sun is at just the right angle, sharp sunlight bounces off the moon's surfaces and every feature is multiplied. Here, shadows are not shadowy, the sun does not cast an empty black outline of itself as it does on Earth but a replication of the thing itself: a replication of something which already exists as if it were a silhouette: a silhouette, then, of a silhouette. And yet, for all its seeming eeriness, the moon to me is an intimate place, a child's planet, a safe haven, a comforting, simple, untroubled place; the moon's weak gravitational pull just strong enough to provide a reassuring sense of up and down, the weakness of the field seeming to encourage play. For all its dust-covered rocky solidity, under the influence of the moon's gentle gravitational pull its surface is transformed into a trampoline, and as on a trampoline I cannot help but laugh, as if the moon has been lonely without us, as if play stirs life and memory.

In zero gravity everyone is equal, at least from that perspective.

It was time to flee his native Germany. For a time he settled in Italy, teaching at the Scuola Superiore in Milan. In 1936 he realised that he must flee again. The composer collected together whatever manuscripts he could lay his hands on and buried them in a large metal chest somewhere near the cathedral. He fled to Russia, and then to Switzerland, where he lived as a refugee throughout the war. In 1943 he completed what would be his last composition, a fourth string quartet. Although he would live for another thirty years he wrote no more music, his spirit broken, he said, by Nazism. Whatever printed scores were circulating in Germany were destroyed by the SS, even the copperplates on which the music had been engraved were melted down.

The area where the chest had been buried was heavily bombed several times during the course of the war. He believed that his music must have been destroyed.

After the war, he made a living as a conductor, a good conductor not a great one.

In 1965, during the course of some excavations around the cathedral, the chest was discovered and returned to its owner.

In what state the manuscripts inside the chest now existed it was impossible to tell. The fear that they had turned to dust exceeded his hope that they had survived intact. He decided not to open the chest.

He died eight years later, the chest still unopened.

Soon after, his widow broke the padlocks. The scores were perfectly preserved.

You exist – of course you do – but you are not what you think you are; which is to say that what you see is an illusion: a relationship between what looks like a self at the end of the universe where you find yourself – here, now – and the universe itself. But there is no you, and there is no universe, only your relationship to what, if you could be outside that relationship would be . . . well, you cannot say. Or, rather, you can and do say since you can imagine what is not and cannot be.

Alan Turing so worried about the future that he bought two bars of silver and buried them. After the war had ended, he couldn't remember where. And there, presumably, they still lie, somewhere under a post-war housing development in Bletchley.

In 1867 the musicologist George Grove went to Vienna with his friend the composer Arthur Sullivan in search of lost Schubert manuscripts. Schubert dead for almost forty years. Found at the bottom of a cupboard, 'and in the farthest corner', a bundle of music books two feet high, carefully tied round, and black with the undisturbed dust of nearly half a century. What had been discovered, rediscovered rather, was all of the incidental music to the ballet *Rosamunde*. After just two performances the score had been tied up and put away, where it had remained until now.

Kairos: the right moment.

Matching those rare occasions when you bump by accident into someone you know, must be the greater number of occasions when you *almost* bump into someone you know. Just as you glanced her way, she rounded the corner. You once walked right past someone you were at school with, but you did not recognise each other. Think of all those photographs that exist in the world in which you can be discerned in the background. But by whom?

What is there out there that is waiting to be found and will one day be found?

What is there out there that is waiting to be found and will never be found?

VIII

FRAGMENTS

(i)   *When I find myself in the company of scientists, I feel like a shabby curate who has strayed by mistake into a drawing room full of dukes.*

(ii)   *Like many intellectuals, he was incapable of saying a simple thing in a simple way.*

(iii) *There was a moment's silence, such as often follows the triumph of rationalism.*

(iv) *She is one of those persons who will squeeze into the same partition of a revolving door with you, on the pretext of causing less trouble.*

(v)   *When I think about Religion at all, I feel as if I would like to found an order for those who cannot believe: the Confraternity of the Fatherless one might call it, where an altar, on which no taper burned, a priest, in whose heart peace had no dwelling, might celebrate with unblessed bread and a chalice empty of wine. Everything to be true must become a religion. And agnosticism should have its ritual no less than faith.*

(vi)   *And why, after all, may not the world be so complex as to consist of many interpenetrating spheres of reality, which we can approach in alternation by using different conceptions and assuming different attitudes.*

(vii) *I have in late years sometimes thought that it might be possible to construct a system of theology or even a religion around the idea of love, if that idea were extended somewhat beyond its usual application, and approached in a certain way.*

(viii) *I have a terrible need for religion. So I go outside at night to paint the stars.*

COMMENTARY

There were miracles once. Not that long ago. Ghosts were more common then and more violent than they are now. Every town and village had its witches and warlocks, its wise men, wizards and shamans. They knew how to fly, become invisible, walk on water, foresee death, know the past and future, enter the minds of others, and understand the language of animals. Bushes no longer burn. Seas are no longer parted. In these days of measurement only the tiniest rents in the fabric of reality. Now magic hardly exists anywhere in the world. There are just a few men and women left who know how to control the world's energies to their own ends.

Sometimes you wish you had devoted your life to studying some closely defined range of interactions between some specific types of protein molecules in some specific type of cell.

He says that the human brain will one day understand itself. What can this mean? Is it the brain alone that understands? What of the body and the neurons that flow from the brain and interface the world? He says that he thinks it more likely that we will understand the brain than the principles of cosmology. But aren't they, you long to say to him, different perspectives on the same problem?

You believe that this is all there is. What you see is what you get. Logically, you know that life is all the more precious for being these moments only and no others, but you cannot balance the infinities.

Homoousion: of the same essence. Not to be confused with homoiousian: of a similar essence. Who cares? I care.

If you had told me four billion years ago that one day there would be life on Earth, I would have laughed in your face.

A thought experiment. In a balance, place the Earth on one side and the universe on the other. Which side goes down? Are you sure?

There are no real laws, not really, not in society, not in nature, but you have agreed to pretend that there are and to act accordingly. Freeing though to know that the best that can be managed is pretence.

There is no perspective to be had. There is no fixed point. There is nowhere to attach the fulcrum.

Over here, a universe of simple laws. Over there, beings of flux, confusion and contradiction.

The extended time of whales and the compressed time of flies are as nothing compared to the slow tick of geological time and the evanescence of quantum time. Such permanence, such brevity: unimaginable, except that imagining is what you do. You can even imagine what is not possible. You can imagine being on the outside looking in.

You say this is like that and that is like this. You make your world out of comparisons. All it took was for someone to insist that something was the case – to say to someone else, *that* is a hedgehog, or indeed to say, that is *not* a hedgehog but something that looks like a hedgehog – and for the someone else to agree or disagree. And so did you begin to feel both less alone and more alone.

Here a match struck in the dark, there a star shining in the firmament. Hello out there, anyone else able to pull off that trick?

Even the most mundane memory – of a view of a mountain, say – is not a record, but a feeling. What it is a feeling of is hard to say, but if pressed you might at last admit that it is like the feeling of something else.

You decided to put your faith in the transcendence of science and of mathematics.

The laws of nature have been waiting out all eternity on the off chance that they might be found out. Or so you thought. Repeated expeditions in search of them began to suggest to you that maybe the laws were not laws after all but the means to an end, perhaps even, you began to fear, *the* end.

Another time, on this occasion searching for some mathematical proof or other – to do with prime numbers you seem to remember, you forget what exactly – you stumbled on some great tunes. Admittedly many of the best ones had already been bagged by explorers who had come before, but there were some really good ones still lying around. What you cannot know is that the best tunes of all will never be discovered. It's just the way things are sometimes.

Is there a better story to be told than the never-ending story of the world as it appears to be? You here, everything else over there. And yet how lonely it has made you.

There was a time, and it was not that long ago, when almost anyone could make a significant discovery. Now nature hides. Experimentation gets harder and harder. You become more determined. Just a little bit more. Nature too becomes more determined. You accumulate the results of more and more measurements, and the physical laws become less pliant, more rigid, more like laws. Soon you will not be able to remember what the world was like before; you will lose the ability to see the world as it once was.

Are you arrogant enough to suppose that if all human beings disappeared, then reality itself would be switched off as if it were a light? *You're missing the point. What disappears is only an idea of what reality is: whatever that best idea is at the time. What is arrogant is your belief that at bottom we know anything about anything. Do you really believe in some kind of absolute reality that human beings have somehow managed to describe and isolate, that has been brought out of the shadows, an eternal monument to their intelligence?*

Sometimes you wonder if you wouldn't feel more comfortable if you were to make a different approach. No tree, no forest. No world, no universe.

Out of the workings of the cock's crow, he said, I will describe the sun. You might, but it is a very long way round.

The real world exists, that much is clear, but it is not what you think it is. No matter what you think it is, it is not that.

Clearly the universe is full of meaning. But the meaning of the meaning?

You have always wanted to be one of those people who on a cold clear night might point confidently at the constellations by name, but you are not that person and you will never be that person. You prefer to be indoors in bed.

Whatever it is that you recollect of the past and conjure up in imagination – whether life that is seconds gone or long gone – is remembered only from some particular vantage point. If everything is not to collapse into meaningless relativism you must choose some perspective, a point of view. Close up, you see only the details and not the undercurrents, from far enough away you might see almost anything.

At a party I overheard someone say, 'Such clever elementary particles, to have within them the *Matthew Passion* and Michelangelo's ceiling.' It was all I could do not to rush up and hug him. I was so happy I decided to go straight home.

He was quoting some recent study the results of which, he said, conclusively proved the inefficacy of prayer. You were not so much listening to him as observing him. His face was distorted, hideous. Odd words and phrases: mumbo-jumbo, naiveté, Father Christmas, the slavery of the Church, fear, children. His anger like a bore tide ready to sweep away anyone or anything that stood in its way. Nobody said a word.

I can win this game, I think to myself. The art is not to get involved. Get involved and you have already lost.

She had seen him before at parties, the man who has devoted his life to good causes, or so he says of himself. She is amused by his attempt to leave the room unnoticed. He is one of those self-proclaimed introverts who signal their invisibility wildly. She pictures his ego, an inflated balloon that fills any room he occupies, but with so little substance to it that it might easily be pricked at any moment of her choosing. Even worse, she thinks to herself, much more dangerous, both substance and inflated ego. Writers in this category. One in particular comes to mind. Thrashes about the world like an empty ocean tanker, shoving aside everything in his path.

Her departing guest is now crouched almost, sidling toward the door with exaggerated high small steps. He is turned, walking crabwise backwards and waving. His waving hand is up by his face making the tiniest gesture side to side. He stumbles into the small table by the door and knocks over that vase, the one she had had to hunt down because he had come with flowers and with instructions that they needed to be put into water as soon as possible.

Nothing happens that any two people might precisely agree on, except perhaps in physics, and not always even then. But you go on trying anyway. Every conversation, every shared cup of tea an attempt to come to some sort of agreement.

He says of miracles, 'Which is more likely: that the laws of nature are temporarily suspended, or that the witness is deceived or lying?' All very well, but you can't help feeling that life is pleasanter when we are more inclined to believe people than not.

Of course there are frauds, but there are frauds everywhere. What is more surprising is how few of them there are, and how genuine most people at least intend to be. Even politicians are romantics, most of them, at least to begin with, determined to make the world a better place, if anything not cynical enough, if anything too naive, at least to begin with. Anyone can be a cynic. It takes courage to be a naïf.

Why should the walls not talk or birds speak Greek? Not everyone tunes into the world at the same frequency.

He has an answer for everything, like one of those smug pundits you come across on the radio or on TV who always has an opinion – delivered with assured vapidity – no matter what the subject: global warming, the latest dance moves, that underrated nineteenth-century Russian novelist, what colour trainers this season.

Someone once asked her, What does God say to you when you pray? Nothing, she said. He listens. And what do you say to God, the questioner persisted? I don't say anything, she said. I listen.

We have recently worked out how to retrieve the vibrations that these ancient walls have soaked up over the centuries. It is hard to work out exactly what is being said. The techniques are still crude. It's only a murmur we can hear, the ghosts of past conversations. We are closing in on the sensitives, the spokesperson says, but we haven't quite got there yet.

Out of fear, inoculating yourself from the harsh truth. Nothing, only material things. Not a real man otherwise. Stand up to the world as it is, not how you want it to be. *Why should you get to arbitrate? To see the world as fundamentally more mysterious than it seems to be is not a flight from reality. Do you not see what you do when you put a limit on what the universe can be? Theologians have been pointing out for ages that whatever God is, existence cannot be one of His qualities. You used to say that the world is made out of stuff. Now you say it is a wave of probability that somehow lies outside of time and space. Is that any less outrageous?*

Make a list of your gods, favourite first.

Her friend turned to Catholicism. He was at a particular low point in his life. A priest had said to him, God loves you no matter what.

'God loves you for yourself,' Yeats said to Lady Goolsbee, 'but I love you for your yellow hair.'

If God is love is all of your religion, why say anything else?

Pilate or Jesus? 'All men are bad', or 'all men are good'. 'What is truth?' or 'Let he who is without sin cast the first stone.' Relativism or universal laws.

I agree that God does not exist, but is that the end of the matter or its beginning? God is beyond understanding. That seems like a good place to start. Not to you of course. You are a fundamentalist. You know God as your personal saviour. You say you are nothing, but you mean everyone else of course. And not you either. You are a physicist. You, too, do not believe in God, though in order to prove your modesty you do believe in aliens.

Familist: member of a sixteenth-century Dutch sect that asserted that religion consists in love not faith.

There have been hundreds of thousands of witnesses: alien encounters, alien abductions, but for you the wrong kind of evidence, the wrong class of witness.

How dreadful, you now think, if it were actually possible to become an entirely different person. What then would be the point of having been the person that you once were?

At church how you loved that morning and evening prayer: *We have erred, and strayed from thy ways like lost sheep. We have followed too much the devices and desires of our own hearts. We have offended against thy holy laws. We have left undone those things which we ought to have done; And we have done those things which we ought not to have done; And there is no health in us. But thou, O Lord, have mercy upon us, miserable offenders.* How you loved to acknowledge that you were nothing, and in such glorious language.

You are not that kind of scientist. You are a believer. When you first arrived here, you said it was like breathing the air of another planet. You once said to me that it is your firm belief that one day human beings will indeed breathe the air of another planet, the air of elsewhere, not bottled air but air freely breathed under a sky, a man-made, man-engineered sky probably. You told me that it is important that humans survive not just for themselves, not just so that science may continue its march towards infinity, but for the sake of Creation. God needs us to survive, you said, otherwise, what is there? Just a nothing that eventually fell back into nothingness. You said you did not know if there is life elsewhere: other lives to give God meaning, but that it was your belief there must be. You said, What a burden otherwise.

You turned your back on religion and found self-abnegation elsewhere. How often have you heard them tell you that you – miserable human offender – are not privileged in any way, that you are not at the centre of things, not at the centre of anything.

I cannot help but notice that there are no aliens and so relax. Darling, I feel divine.

You speculate that aliens, when you meet them, if you ever meet them, might prove to be more intelligent than you are, or more powerful, but what if they turn out to be kinder and more loving?

There is alien life across the universe. Some of those aliens have stumbled upon the scientific method. And so there are investigators across the universe coming to the same conclusions that are being reached here on Earth by our own local investigators, everywhere uncovering the universal laws of nature. But what if the question of whether or not there are aliens remains undecided or turns out, for lack of evidence, to be undecidable? Embarrassing you would have thought for our local investigators to go on telling us that we are of no account, not knowing for sure that they aren't themselves not only the most privileged observers in the universe, but possibly even the only ones.

How you long to be contacted by aliens. How you long to be seen from an outside perspective. How you long to see what you cannot see for yourself. And yet, the agony of being seen.

IX

FRAGMENTS

(i)   Who, who can turn the skies back, and begin again?

(ii) My solitude is sublime. The roaring of the wind is my wife
      and the stars through the window are my children.

(iii) The further afield you go, the more you are going home . . .
      It is as if the gods put us down with a certain arbitrary glee
      in the wrong place and what we seek is who we really ought
      to be.

(iv) If I really love the world, I will fit myself to it, rather than
      make it fit me.

COMMENTARY

Augury: the flight of an eagle, particularly as a prediction of the future.

They said to Aeschylus, a house will fall on top of you and kill you. A likely story! Did the prospect seem to him so farfetched that he refused to worry about it? Or did he think, there's nothing to be done about it; I do not know how a house might fall on me, but if that is what has been prophesied then so be it, no point in worrying? An eagle flying overhead dropped the tortoise shell it was carrying. Aeschylus died. Did Aeschylus look up and see the eagle? Was there time to think, Ah, an eagle, an augury of something? But what is it that the eagle is carrying in its talons? What is it that the eagle has let go of? Was there time, or did the final blow come from nowhere? Had the gods argued among themselves whether or not Aeschylus should be in on the joke? Either way, the gods had a good laugh that day.

You were a child walking to town with your mother. It was a hot day. You happened to glance down a side street and you caught his eye. He looked at you and you looked at him. With a jolt something was exchanged between you and then you looked away. You didn't know then that there were people who lived on the street, nor did you yet understand any of the various reasons why people might end up there.

The woman in church who sat up front, one of the half-dozen at Evensong, all women, all old, or what I saw as old then. Afterwards I couldn't quite remember which one she had been. She lived on a hilltop farm I heard them say, a lonely figure, kept herself to herself. Drowned in a well. Had she lowered herself in or dropped like a stone?

I reached a certain age and the thread that had run through my life broke. For a time I disappeared from myself.

He says, did something traumatic happen to you when you were three? You are tipped back in his chair. The fillings from the teeth in one side of your face have been removed, the other side left for another day. He is smoking at his desk. This happened some time ago, but not that long ago. He really shouldn't have been smoking. You love him for it. At the same time, you are terrified that you might gag on the metalwork he has left in your mouth.

Ever since your breakdown, your rationalism has been challenged. You were now game for anything. Energy workshops. Past-life regression. You tried not to laugh when, in a mews house in Holland Park, she started dancing around you in Native American headwear waving a burning torch of sage. Another time, you lying on the floor, he told you that he would start to move energy around your body and that you might or might not feel something. Not wanting to embarrass him you wondered if you had better twitch now and again just to be polite. Moments later your entire body was undulating uncontrollably. Another time, an Indian mystic as if out of central casting approached you in the street. Brightly coloured flowing robes, saffron turban, beaming smile. No one about, the street entirely empty of people and traffic even though you were in central London. He walked straight up to you and took your hand. He looked you in the eye and said, You love too much. Even your singing teacher, you soon discovered, possessed esoteric powers.

In a quiet voice, barely looking up from his desk your dentist asks you for your full name and the year of your birth. He writes the answers on a piece of paper. It is shortly after that he asks, Did something traumatic happen to you when you were three? You hardly pause to wonder why he should be asking you such a curious question. You trust him. Perhaps you wondered if he had seen evidence in your mouth of some infant trauma. It's funny you should say that, you say. And then you burst into tears. Not at all like you. You are not even sure what you were going to say. That's all I need to know, says your dentist, who, you are beginning to suspect, is also a magician. A lot of emotion gets trapped in our teeth. Before I fill your teeth up again I wanted to see if I could release some of that old energy. He hands you a paper handkerchief. You take it and blow your nose. Now, says your dentist-who-is-also-a-magician, let's fill those teeth.

A sphere that is falling through space, in a solar system that is falling around the gravitational centre of a cluster of galaxies, that is itself falling . . . that is itself falling . . . until the idea of falling comes to an end. Because if the universe is falling, what exactly is it that is falling, and into what?

As a child you used to lie face down, stretched out on the ground, as if holding on. And then at some point you grew out of the habit.

You picked up a cylinder of cardboard and looked through it as if it were a telescope. Your friend put his face at the other end and you looked at each other. The cylinder was just wide enough to cover your faces. You looked at each other down the tube as if at opposite ends of a tunnel. His face filled your whole field of vision, and yours his. You both started laughing. Then something odd started to happen to you. You began to shake. You felt hot and then cold and faint. You were looking at yourself. You were inside your friend's head looking at yourself, and he and you were the same person. And you knew that if he and you were the same person then everyone was the same person.

Atonement: the state of being At One. The reconciliation, brought about by Christ's sacrifice, of God and human beings.

He said he was prepared to wait for a materialist explanation. You found him in the waiting room, centuries later. Dead. By then, what had been in need of an explanation had been forgotten about altogether.

Not that long ago, when all the stars were glued onto a single revolving orb, what did it feel like then to be a human being? How cosy the universe must have seemed, vaulted above like a cathedral, not at all forbidding. Did the stars then proclaim not the infinity of space but their beauty, as if for the sheer delight of humankind? Or perhaps the pinprick stars shining through the world's enclosing canopy even then felt unimaginably far away.

You see the sun rise over the horizon of the ocean, you sense the planet turning, you hear the thrum of your brain, you feel vertiginous.

Three times the cock crowed, and three times he denied Christ.

I should have changed my friends but instead I changed my nature. I acted one way but I was persuaded that I ought to act another, with the result that ever after I was alienated from my own people, both in the lands from where I had come and in the lands to where I had travelled. Only later by travelling even further out would I find myself again at home. It was my own fault. You seem to be yourself now, he said to me. Yes, but only because I am in another place, and because I love you.

Her account made it sound almost Biblical. Even before it actually started to happen, she could sense that it was about to happen, like those animals that detect a coming earthquake or tsunami. It was as if a hot wind had suddenly roared into the room, making its way directly to her and entering her body via the soles of her feet, exiting again out of the top of her head. All the nerves in her body began to fire. She shook all over.

She said she would get a fever by looking at a peach, that she heard a fly landing on the table as a dull thud in her ear. She developed severe panic attacks. She said that she could bring them on just by thinking unsettling thoughts. One of her severest attacks happened after she had been daydreaming about a time after her death when she had been reincarnated as a rabbit, a pet rabbit in a hutch unable to communicate.

To be depressed is like falling down a well, the world becomes distant, visible but unreachable. The greatest horror of all, realising that there is no escape, not even from your own self. There is nothing to do but accept that you are at the bottom of a well. And then, gradually, you begin to look up, and so long as you do not struggle, you realise that you are actually quite safe here. The world is out there and you are protected from it. After a while you begin to feel quite comfortable giving in to whatever terrors beset you. You do not die. And then, one night, on a particularly clear, dark, cloudless, moonless night you discover what the ancients discovered before you, that from the bottom of a well you can see more stars than you can normally see.

Later jumping out of planes, for the sense of falling and for the sense of letting go of the ego, to be held by the air, in those moments to cheat death. I know that it is the parachute that will save me, but what I feel is the air cradling me. It's not the falling that kills you.

You were oversensitive, vulnerable, too trusting, you tell yourself. You were deluded. You were ill. Doubt has returned. You are again sceptic and realist. What happened then wasn't quite enough. Is it ever?

There are limits to what you are prepared to believe, in either direction. Care has to be taken about what is said and to whom. Much is better not said at all. For a time you stood at the gates to a world you had not known existed, a world that you would have mocked from the vantage point of your former self. The whispered secrets are not secrets because they are inaudible but because we mostly choose not to listen.

What kind of person finds herself at the bottom of a well, unless she has fallen in, or been pushed in? Did she realise that she had discovered a repeatable and universal fact about the world that might bring people together? Of course not. Was she delighted to see more stars? Very possibly.

The world has a way of closing in on us, she said. The future is petrifying. Resist the world and we become immovable, like stone. Let the world happen to you. Move through it lightly, as if pushing aside one veil after another. Meet a rock as a rock, she said, and it will become even more rocklike. Where there are rocks meet them as veils, and as veils is how they will reveal themselves. The secret is to play the world at its own game. Love the world and shout for more of it. The world is intolerant of ambivalence. Like a good New Yorker, you have to say what you want without ambiguity, and out loud. She said, All you have to do is ask.

In the grand hall a formal debate is in progress. All men. From what you can overhear, you gather that they are talking about collective reproducible evidence. You leave through a side door and find yourself in a winding corridor that leads into other winding corridors. Hardly knowing how you got here – as if you have wandered by accident into the meeting place of some exclusive and secret society – you find yourself in a small, mostly bare room in which a single silent figure is sitting, expectant-looking, as if she has been waiting for you. She does not speak but you tell her everything that you have discovered about yourself. You tell her that it may not be evidence that will do for anyone else but that it is proof enough for you. You tell her that you might be better off not sharing it, except perhaps with those who have also wandered onto the same path.

Throughout history the young, because they are young, have been treated as if they are of no account. It would not be surprising if, as a consequence, they were to think the same thing of themselves.

And if now it is no longer terror you feel at night, still you can induce that frisson of the existential angst that gives you the sense of free fall. *None of it can be real. It is all impossible. Even the impossibility of it is impossible.*

X

FRAGMENTS

(i)   History started badly and hav been getting steadily worse.

(ii) Carol told Una, 'Josie's belief in her innocence is her warrant
      for doing harm.' Una said, 'Like America.'

(iii) Not many people have to face the fact that in certain
      circumstances anything is possible.

(iv) Imagining evil is romantic and varied; real evil is gloomy,
      barren, boring. Imagining good is boring; real good is always
      new, marvellous, intoxicating.

(v)   We are turning into animals. I feel it in myself.

COMMENTARY

Every question you ask about the physical universe leads back to the Big Bang. Every question you ask about your own nature leads back to the concentration camp.

Isolate a person, a group, a race, a nation. And then what, the entire world?

Whatever happened to that family we used to talk to most days, who lived a few doors away? They have gone now. We were told that they have gone to another country, and though we do not really believe it, we will believe it anyway because we do not need to think about that family any more, and it is better that they are gone because there is now more for those of us who remain. They have gone to another country. They are not here.

We the chosen, if only by default, for not being the others, not being Jews, not being homosexual, not being Hutu, not being Catholic.

Not religion this time but pseudoscience. A programme of racial purification that was bound to fail in the end. There are no boundaries that separate them from the rest of you. They are not things. There is no them.

The orderly way or the chaotic way. Same effect.

You know the names of the killers, you rarely remember the names of their victims, even more rarely do you remember the names of those who lived quiet lives, not achieving anything much except not killing.

A random day in history, somewhere on planet Earth: hundreds of people, most of the population of the township that had been their home, are brutally massacred. Mothers disembowelled, children mutilated. No one notices.

It's what you humans are good at, or can get to be good at, used to be better at, being sensitive to the smallest signs. You lost the power during those years. You looked away. You ignored what was in front of your noses. You learned the art of obliviousness. What masters you became! You did not see. You chose not to see; did not talk about what you chose not to see, until eventually you had made for yourselves a new reality. And yet still there were times – odd moments – when some kind of exchange took place. There were times when the slightest facial movement was enough to tell you everything you needed to know.

When I think about the history of the world, I see a vast mountain made out of the dead bodies of the slain. Blood courses down the mountainsides. From time to time whole sides of the mountain collapse. Millions of compacted skeletons fall away in a single mass, crashing to the mountain's base: a wider base on which to build the mountain higher still.

They hanged men outside your office, sometimes women and children too, always in the same place. Saboteurs, they said they were; vermin to be caught and destroyed, they said. In your dreams it was always the same man you saw. He did not struggle. Not entirely true. There were gestures that he made, but they were so tiny they were hard to read. You knew in the dream that, as tiny as they were, they were gestures of resistance, but he struggled on such a minute scale that it was like watching a puppet show put on by the most brilliant puppet master, one who knows that it is in the smallest movements that the illusion of animation is most convincingly created.

We didn't think it possible, says this generation, having forgotten what was all too real to the generation that had come before.

Would you jump off a bridge if he told you to, your mother says? He has not asked you to jump off a bridge, but he has asked you to do something stupid that might have caused you harm, and your mother is understandably angry. You see her anger and not the fear that is behind it. Or perhaps you feel the fear even if you do not see it. Because you know that arguing with your mother will only make things worse, you say, 'No', sullenly, even though you know that the answer is probably 'Yes'. So in thrall are you to him that you might do anything. It is only by chance that you are neither the little boy who walks away, mesmerised by the teenagers who have shown an interest in him, nor one of the teenagers taking his hand and leading him to the railway track.

You stay strong in order that you may bear the fate of being loved. To be truly loved is a terrible burden.

Negotiation, it turned out, could only take you so far. After all those years it had taken you to a point where both of you were exhausted. You had exhausted all possible arguments and defences and had exhausted yourselves. Each of you had arrived at his own sticking post. You had travelled far from where you had set out from, but now it was time to part and to travel your separate ways. For years you could hardly bear to be separated even for a moment. You did not know it yet, but you would hardly ever see each other ever again. Love too had been exhausted. The enzyme of your love had been all used up, never to be made again. Of course, if you chose to you might recollect the love that had been, but neither of you is a person who spends much time looking back. The time had been, and now is gone. There had been only the one way to get to your separate futures, the necessary path you had for a time travelled together before parting forever.

In the end Natasha marries Pierre. In the end Levin does not commit suicide. Better Pierre than Andrei. Better Levin than Anna.

Abelard and Heloise, Romeo and Juliet, Bonnie and Clyde, Hindley and Brady. Another love story that ended badly for all concerned. Everything grasped too firmly turns to the dark, even love. You say everywhere, in your religions, on TV, in your songs and writings, repeatedly in your conversations, that love conquers all. It is fortunate that you do not actually believe it. Love, what is done in your name!

The crowd unites behind a single grievance. You find yourself doing what you would not believe possible. You shout words you would never have dreamt of using. And then, why not, might as well pick up a stone.

Did you shoot the Christian in the head because everyone else was doing it?

Oh him, she says. He's one of those people who, if you and I found ourselves together on a train on the way to the camps, would be there on the platform, recently promoted, waving regretfully, a shrug of the shoulders that says, 'I know. It's fucked up, but what can I do?' And as the train pulls away from the station we wonder, Is that a handkerchief? Is he crying?

Later he became a famous pianist; as a child he had been imprisoned, along with his mother, in a concentration camp. A guard who had heard him playing Schubert on his accordion – isn't it always Schubert? – one day took the boy and his mother to the station, put them on a train, tossed the accordion in after them and wished them luck.

In the train carriage. If I absolutely had to sleep with someone, who would it be? Or the other game I play: who among them would betray me and who save me?

The day at school assembly when the deputy head pulled a boy out of his seat by his hair. One of the brave ones as I see the boy now, even though he was a bully and always in trouble. The boy fought back and the deputy head fought harder, the bigger bully. The boy twisted and then fell quiet like a mouse playing dead, another of the world's victims. The deputy head scoured the room looking for trouble. The moment passed. I like to think that somewhere – in some parallel universe – I stood up in protest. But perhaps in the end it is better that there was only that one opportunity and I did not take it.

Years ago, she crossed your path. Today, at this very moment, she is remembering you. She is recalling something she overheard you saying. You were on a train, travelling to York with a friend. Because of what you said that day she has nursed a grievance against you for years. You have no memory of the conversation nor of the journey, certainly no memories of her. You will never remember anything about that day.

I have not forgotten them: the woman who criticised me for not standing out of the way as she attempted to get out of the crowded tube; the man, whom she did not know, who agreed with her; the woman who accused me of not having a ticket and of following her – too closely she said – through the tube barrier. I think of them often. I want revenge.

'I couldn't sleep all night for thinking of that ghastly horror camp! – I thought he meant Cyril Clatworthy.' The audience did not laugh this time.

A voice is saying, What are you doing in this room? I am standing in the doorway, appalled, unable to speak. I am perhaps nine years old. I had been curious to see my friend Carol's bedroom. Of course I had to look. Was she a friend? Carol was very, very shy. Was that even her name? I thought she looked like a doll. Very straight black hair. I can't hear her voice. I hear a doll's voice. Her father is a policeman. I had been invited round to her house, and now her mother has caught me out. Coming back from the toilet, I passed the open bedroom door then stepped back. I was bending forward to peer into the room: so pink, so many soft toys, so clean. There is something wrong. Everything is too ordered, too tidy. It doesn't look as if anyone has ever played in there. I feel sad. Sadness is leaking out of the room. Carol, like the room, is too tidy, too groomed, her black patent leather shoes too shiny, spotless, her black hair too black and shiny and spotless too, too sharply cut, her face too round, her skin too pale. I don't remember ever seeing her smile. This room is private, Carol's mother is saying to me, you should not be in here. She sends me back to the kitchen where some kind of birthday celebration is taking place, except that that must have been on another occasion not this one. In my memory I must have time travelled. Stepping from the corridor into the kitchen suddenly there are lots of other children my own age. Looking back, I wonder if I had known that there was something not quite right about Carol's parents, had not been able to articulate it. Now I tell this story to myself: Carol is being sexually abused by her father; her mother knows but is in denial. I say to myself that the mother's attempts to minutely control the small part of the world that she can control is how her denial has manifested itself.

Carol's mother is doing the rounds in the kitchen carrying a plate of sandwiches. Not that one, she says to me. Take the nearest one. I do as I am told. Carol's mother is smiling, and it is then that I understand that even a smile can be used as a weapon. Again I say nothing. I have nothing to say, and perhaps instinctively know that silence is the best option for a child. Or perhaps it was my apparent self-composure that infuriated her. Not that I ever thought of myself as at all self-possessed, but I was observant, and formed judgements. I decided in that moment that Carol's mother was a vicious and cruel woman. No, I had not decided it; I knew it to be true.

XI

FRAGMENTS

(i) *The best piety is to enjoy – when you can. You are doing the most then to save the earth's character as an agreeable planet.*

(ii) *What do we live for if it is not to make life less difficult to each other?*

(iii) *Gently . . . didst thou amble round the little world of thy pleasures, jostling no creature in thy way.*

(iv) *But all the doctrine, which he taught and gave, / Was clear as heav'n from whence it came / . . .* Love God, and love your neighbour. Watch and pray. / Do as ye would be done unto.

(v) *It has been observed that there are actually two long-range revolutions in progress throughout the world. To the first, that material revolution wherein the unjustly deprived are demanding their share of the affluence made possible by modern technological means of production, Brecht is outstandingly relevant. To the second, the ensuing revolution of consciousness wherein the outwardly secure and satisfied grope with basic questions about the truth of their lives and the purposes their freedom should be put to, Ibsen remains equally relevant.*

(vi) *Materialism means simply the denial that the moral order is eternal, and the cutting off of ultimate hopes; spiritualism means the affirmation of an eternal moral order and the letting loose of hope. Surely here is an issue genuine enough for anyone who feels it . . .'*

(vii) *Visionary dreariness.*

COMMENTARY

You want just a few nice things. How many, and how nice?

The universe expanded; things became more complex.

Not the questing for the objects of desire. A desire fulfilled is no longer a desire. A desire is fulfilled and another desire fills the vacuum, abhorred as all vacuums are. And then another desire, and another. And so it is that either your desires remain unfulfilled or you come to understand something about the nature of desire itself. Attachment, suffering. You get it, but now what?

You remember a time when no one had had any money, and there had been nothing to buy. No one owned anything. And then a new era was ushered in. At first no one had known what to make and no one had known what to buy. Things were made for the sake of the making, and things were bought for the sake of the buying. Time passed and you got better at knowing what to make, and people got better at knowing what to buy, but then even that era soon came to an end.

'I'll say it again,' he says. 'The rich *are* happier. On the whole. Who wouldn't be happier knowing each morning that a day of freedom lies ahead. Fashionable clothes, a good haircut, fresh food, light and warmth, a pleasant sofa on which to lie and listen to music or to read a novel. The wants of most people are not monstrous, but somehow the simple life after which we all hanker has become beyond the reach of all but the richest among us, No one dares put a figure on it. Not now. Jane Austen did. And Virginia Woolf. How much, would you say, how much would you need to live a simple, civilised, middle-class life in the twenty-first century. In London,' he adds, jabbing a finger to indicate that he requires an answer. 'Does anyone need to be a billionaire? Who was it said that everything is about sex except sex, which is about power? Update people: everything is about money except money, which is about power.'

She loathes him when he is in this mode, even though she nearly always agrees with what he has to say. There is something about his tone that she cannot bear. Is it the man thing? Mansplaining? The word itself makes her feel more kindly towards him, as if having made her diagnosis she is able to be more forgiving.

She thinks she had better look as if she is considering an answer. She needn't have bothered. He is again in full flow, as if addressing a public meeting. How to make sense of her mixed feelings about him. She really does love him when he isn't on, but he is always on, even when it is just the two of them. He talks to her as if she were a public meeting. His ego is a hard shell that imprisons a finer, deeper self, she decides. The shell separates his better self from the world, imprisoning both. It is a double prison that makes his life hell. But is his life hell? He doesn't behave as if his life were hell. Perhaps I'm on the wrong track, she thinks. I want to believe that he knows that he is in hell but does not know how to escape. She begins to feel more kindly towards him once more. If only he might show a little kindness, even if only to himself. But no, she decides, he's just a little shit and I will have to leave him.

'One hundred and fifty thousand pounds. At least,' he says. 'There was a time when I used to earn more than that. It was the happiest time in my life,' apparently forgetting the fact that he had been miserable. He seems to have forgotten too that when he could bear the misery no longer, he had voluntarily brought that period of his life to an abrupt end, and that it was then that he had had his nervous breakdown.

Now she wondered if the Period of Things would turn out to have been a brief interregnum between very different eras: the time of nothing, and the time which seemed to be fast approaching when just about everything that anyone might reasonably need was all contained within a single, immensely complex but inexpensive device.

He is twenty-two years old. He tells her that he has never bought a CD or a DVD, never sent a letter and never received one, has never bought a stamp, never written a cheque, has hardly ever bought books. Shelter, food and clothes, of course, otherwise the latest electronic devices. Food was Soylent, clothes came from Uniqlo or H&M. Cheap. The electronic device however had to be top of the range. House ownership was accepted as being outside the reach of his generation unless there was family money, which in his case there was. For the rest, the early death of parents was always a possibility but an increasingly slim one. How many years is added to life expectancy every decade?

She can't remember, but it's significant. And then if you do live into your nineties, life expectancy actually goes up. Young people seem to know how to get almost everything for nothing or virtually nothing. They seem to be so much more unburdened than her generation had been. Or is she being too romantic? Her young friend told her that almost everyone he knew was suffering from some kind of anxiety problem, nearly everyone was medicated in some way or another. Everyone knew someone who had committed suicide. Many of them had at least contemplated it at some point.

They seemed to be so much more self-sufficient than she had been at that age, but she wondered how close any of them were to each other. It sounded as if they were lonelier than her generation had been. Was that true? She herself had been excruciatingly lonely as a student and into her twenties, but it felt different somehow. She had had many friends. Was that the difference? Had she been battling another kind of loneliness? Being lonely alone seemed to be the modern fate.

The troubadours would have swooned: a device to bring the beloved distant object close to yet still out of reach. I see him searching the screen, looking, a slight delay before he finds what he is looking for: me. I am holding the screen at arm's length. In the magic glass he is conjured up from thousands of miles distant and held in a place of no location. The intimacy is extraordinary. I do what I would not do in real life. I look straight into his eyes, bring my face right up to his. And yet despite the seeming proximity, I am painfully aware of what I cannot do. I am painfully aware that he is not here and feel his absence all the more keenly. Here he is and here he is not. Existential pornography.

The things of the world evolved at an ever-increasing pace, linearly, geometrically, exponentially, faster still, no fastest function. For a time each generation had thought itself superior to the generation that had come before; now, not better but more isolated. You failed to notice that the mind-stuff of the world had been evolving too. Never mind genes, culture – all your ways of being – had long ago become the prime motor of evolution. Machines and flesh blurred into each other; the world became a coextension of everything.

Pejorist: someone who believes that the world is getting worse.

You confused growth and progress. You ate up the Earth. Eternity is an expensive business. Too expensive for humans.

You live in a universe of abundance. There is more than enough for everyone. The gods sigh.

Of course I believe in progress, she said. I believe in technological progress, just as you do. It's the only kind of progress there is. We broke the circle of nature. Or rather, we opened it out flat and called it eternity, an arrow pointing to the future. The plough came before the steam engine, the steam engine before the combustion engine, the combustion engine before the iPhone. Our tools lie on a line that points towards more elaborate tools to come: an infinite array of tools pointing towards eternity. Better experiments, better theories, better tools, better experiments, better theories, better tools . . . I agree with you, she said, that scientific progress feels like something genuinely novel in the universe. And yet just because there is technological progress it does not follow that there is also economic progress. I mean, just look at the world! That the future will always be better, what a curious belief that is.

Because life has no meaning it does not follow that life is not worth living, tempting as it is, at times, to reach that conclusion. That life has no meaning relieves you of what would otherwise be an intolerable burden.

At the heart of economics lies a question rarely asked: what does it mean to live a meaningful life?

The fear of a life spent pulling the insides out of chickens was what had motivated her to get herself out of her childhood town and to university.

Here's a koan if you will: what would a world of grown-ups look like?

Is there anything more depressing than doing nothing all day. What are people supposed to do in the bright new future, if indeed the bright new future ever arrives?

What are you doing? I'm comparing from around the world the different wiring diagrams of the domestic plug.

What are you doing? I'm listing the popes in order of most evil to most benign. I think they were at their worst in the fifteenth century, though they weren't much better, taken collectively, in the fourteenth.

What are you doing? I'm trying to see if I can fit a marble between each of my toes.

What are you doing? I'm seeing how long it will take to eat this cream cake using only a pin.

What are you doing? I'm cutting out photographs of the most attractive members of the Taliban.

What are you doing? I'm making a list of the top one thousand works of art in any genre. I had Chartres at number 20 but I'm thinking of moving up the *Matthew Passion*. I actually prefer the *John Passion* but if pushed I'd have to admit that the *Matthew* is the greater work. Isn't that often the way: greater not necessarily meaning preferred. It's not every day I want to listen to Beethoven's Ninth, or Britten's *War Requiem*, and yet I can't imagine a day on which I would not want to see, should someone have it to hand, Titian's *Flaying of Marsyas*, or Caravaggio's *Burial of St Lucy*.

What are you doing? Nothing.

In a restaurant somewhere in the home counties, I overhear an old man say, 'So I wrote down everything from when I got up, right up to when I went to bed. I only hope that satisfies her.' Later in the same conversation: 'I fall over twice a day. Four times if I'm wearing my bifocals.'

Donald Judd's advice. Read for three hours every day. Have a bed in every room.

There is no interval. It has been cancelled. They have all gone home. Three of the most consoling sentences in the English language.

Men going outside in order primarily not to be indoors. Footling about and burning rubbish, or sitting on the canal bank not fishing. A pretence of fishing, staring into the middle-distance of their own lives, meditating, keeping sane, not talking, not depressed, just being outside.

In some now forgotten Englishman's diary: It rained yesterday. It rained today. I think it will rain tomorrow.

The two women in front of you at the greengrocer's, one of whom asks the greengrocer for rocket. I am sorry madam but there is no rocket today, the greengrocer tells her. I think I'll shoot myself, she says. Yes, says the woman behind her, it's the end of the world.

Somewhere, always, there is someone laughing, someone living it up, someone having just the best time of it.

Being the playthings of the gods, we should then play the noblest games, said Plato.

Winston Churchill's advice. Never stand when you can sit down, and never sit down when you can lie down.

People have to do something. Or so you say. What then to do about the fact that most people are useless at their jobs. I mean completely useless, so useless it might be better if you simply paid them to do nothing at all.

At first it seems as if the workmen will never arrive, and then as if they will never leave, until, eventually, the moment arrives when it becomes clear that the workmen will not be coming back.

They understand the concept of the infinitesimal. As the job nears completion the remaining tasks become increasingly small but never reduce to nothing. Eventually, the work is abandoned, and the abandoned job *is* the job. In that regard, like writers.

By chance you came across some shepherdesses moving between pastures. What you remember is their insistence that you should know that they considered their lives to be idyllic.

Uberly: from the Latin for udder, the milk of human kindness.

Every breath you inhale contains a few molecules of the air that was once breathed by Julius Caesar. Why pick on him? Why not the same air as a breath once taken by some first-century child who lived peacefully on a fjord in what is now Norway?

An ordinary day out in the countryside. A picnic. A swim in a lake.

Ghosts in the machine hardly goes far enough. You carry with you like a fog the ghost of everything that has gone before. Everything! All history, every war, every life, every conversation that there has ever been, every meal eaten, every window anyone has ever opened, every first breath and every last breath.

Someone the other day told me that they were working to make the world a better place. An activist she called herself. Worthy. Suspicious of worthiness.

To give up the self for family, a nation, the world, the universe. Noble. Suspicious of noble. Prefer to think of quiet lives, unvisited graves, unknown names, not known nor will ever be.

Another banquet at the court of the Esterhazys; a tapestry a decade in the making, a cathedral centuries. The ongoing project – tens of thousands of years – of being human beings – dizzyingly accelerating – surely can't go on like this – not never-ending, however – plenty of warnings. Nothingness. As if there had been none of it all along, none of it at all.

A life lived quietly, attending to the tiny details that culture allows, surely the only way to make sense of the wars that allow periods of peace in which such details might be attended to. It is your duty to be as happy as you possibly can be. For the sake of the millions who died in the war, it seems only polite that those of you who come after should make the most of life.

I want to be among the invisible people.

XII

FRAGMENTS

(i)   It was easy enough to despise the world, but decidedly difficult to find any other habitable region.

(ii) If we could read the secret history of our enemies, we should find in each man's life sorrow and suffering enough to disarm all hostility.

(iii) Done because we are too menny.

(iv) On the other hand, if children are to be so many fewer in the near future than they are today, it is more than ever desirable that they should be of the best attainable quality and thoroughly well nurtured and that nothing of value inherent in them should be wasted.

(v)   Death, a way out of time and space.

COMMENTARY

It's hard enough to fill a weekend let alone eternity. I do hope Heaven spares us that.

On this particular morning I am standing staring into the garden pond hoping to see frogs or newts, and always on the lookout for something unusual, perhaps a fish hatched from eggs accidentally brought in on the feet of some visiting bird. The ghost of a leaf floats up from the pond's murky depths. And then something lying on the bottom of the pond attracts my attention. At first I do not know what it is that I am looking at. As if an optician has inserted just the right lens, the object suddenly comes into sharp focus. And then I see, with absolute clarity, the delicate features of a perfectly drowned field mouse. At any moment the mouse might scuttle away across the floor of the pond so animated does it look, or swim back to the surface and out of its newfound element.

She leans in to her dying lover and says, 'What is the answer?' Her lover says, 'What is the question?'

Favillous: like ash.

I will never die, which makes it all the more shocking when I contemplate those who have, particularly those whom I once knew intimately. The shock is the shock both of realising, without understanding at all what it could mean, that life has been taken away from them, and the callousness of one's own self that has so easily forgotten that they ever existed.

Her house is full of treasures only she values. She will never part with them. No one wants them. Piles of rubbish, newspapers bound and tied, vinegared with cats' piss. Generations of cats long dead. Towers of bulging boxes slumped at improbable angles might crush a person if anyone ever came.

No one wants to live forever. Who wants to live forever? Fundamentalists of one kind or another, anyone with an unbalanced ego, some billionaires, that's who.

Physical traces and memories fade away eventually, only art, you say, lasts forever. I want my life to be an exemplar to no one, witnessed by no one except God, in whom I do not believe.

Cleaning out a kitchen cabinet with her mother, from behind a shelf a piece of paper floated down to the floor. Written on it, in the unmistakable handwriting of her father were the words, Back in Five Minutes. Her father had died three years before. They were speechless.

I do not want this day to end. I know, however, that there is only one day that does not end.

I will drown and no one shall save me. I shall drown and no one will save me. A cry of resolution, and a cry of despair.

Darwin's mother died when he was eight years old. In response to the death of a friend's wife, Darwin wrote that 'never in my life having lost one near relative, I dare say I cannot imagine how severe grief such as yours must be'. He failed to recognise the word mother in a word game. 'There is no such word,' he said.

The pianist on the stage plays his heart out, some Liszt thing that he has been studying for years, for all his life in fact, dizzying, tumbling diamond ropes of notes. What a brain he has fashioned for himself! What hand to brain coordination! No one in the audience is listening, not really. Several people are actually asleep, some others are stifling yawns, most are thinking of something else altogether. The piece reaches an apotheosis, wave after wave of ecstatic melismas until, twenty minutes after the first dramatic opening chords, seemingly impossible running double octaves bring the piece to an ending so abrupt the audience is taken by surprise. Realising that their voluntary torture is at an end what starts as a smattering of applause grows and grows. There are shouts and whistles, stamping of feet. What a relief to be getting home. Please let there be no more than two encores, and short ones. The pianist stands exhausted, rabid with adrenalin, grinning like a hyena, and just then, just at that very moment it hits him that it is all for nothing, none of it is real, the seed of his future despair has been sown. In three months' time he will think about hanging himself.

Even knowing that I would suffer only for an instant, even knowing logically, rationally, that there is no moment beyond that last moment, that there is no moment in which to suffer beyond the moment itself, even knowing this, I construct an elaborate fear: that as the end nears, at the threshold of death, time slows right down, at the moment of death comes to a standstill. From the moment of birth time is slowing down – so my crackpot theory posits – but we only really notice the closer and closer we get to those last moments, in the same way that we don't notice the slowing down of time when we are moving, because the effect is only noticeable at speeds close to the speed of light, and we never are moving that fast. But we do all die. And so, only when those last moments arrive, as they must and will, does the full horror strike us: an instant that lasts an aeon, that last moment – of excruciating pain? – that lasts forever.

Clever virus! But then you did have a several-billion-year head start.

In the nineteenth-century French novel I am reading: he lives, he says, as if his beloved daughter has gone abroad to live in America. Her death means nothing to him.

That voice, those clothes. I see you as if it were yesterday, and not . . . how long ago is it now?

The short haul back to non-existence. No manual. Hardly enough time to learn how to manipulate this machine before the time comes to abandon it again.

Anything that lasts forever grows boring eventually, or, worse, hateful. Constant reinvention keeps the present alive and jolly. We need the young to keep the show on the road.

For centuries the ill had been collected together in one place, with all the obvious risks that that entailed and which did indeed transpire. The old too, the mad, even the very young were all isolated from the rest of society. For reasons of efficiency and safety it was said.

In those years now passed, the virus killed several million human beings before it burned itself out. Though the world's population was not significantly reduced, nevertheless despair took hold.

The young dead are everywhere, as if being old had become a perversion. Bodies litter the streets and canals; in the parks, lying on the grass as if sunbathing; seen dimly through car windows; a young body at the base of almost every tall building, sometimes several. Today it is near freezing; today the smell is bearable.

It was a combination of factors, each of which separately had befallen the world many times before. The Earth had always survived, and survived again even this catastrophe of catastrophes. The time of humans, however, was at an end.

Even the slightest belief in an afterlife might act as a siren call to the lover left behind. A strong belief in the extinction of everything with death might be a stronger call still. At least then there is an end to suffering.

What is it about self-slaughter that is so disturbing? That we are all in it together and the pact has been betrayed. It's anger we feel as much as sorrow.

It's called *Suicide Nights*. It's about a man who every night attempts to commit suicide, but every time he comes to it he thinks of something that is just enough to keep him going for another day. It's a kind of *One Thousand and One Nights*. I'm guessing that by the end he decides to go on living, unless he runs out of reasons by, say, night 527, which would give the novel a modern nihilistic spin.

You are dead, not today as you write this, but one day. Years have passed since you died. But I, your reader, have stumbled across this book and these sentences. You are furious that I am alive and you are dead. You are angry that you will never know what became of the world, angry that you will never know how I came across this book, angry that you will never know what I am making of it, angry that you will never be able to talk to me about it, angry that we will never be friends.

Why wonder if you will escape the ego in death? What about trying to escape it in life? Try imagining yourself as an automaton. You have often imagined yourself as a robot. Or you can try to dissolve yourself into your surroundings, into society, into nature. Imagine dissolving yourself into history. You are everything that came before, at all scales. You try to come into focus for these moments, for this brief span. There is no point of focus, no perspective from which anything ever comes into focus. You are nothing.

We live as if there will always be another summer, another year. Forget that, we live as if there will always be another hour, another minute, another second.

A life that leaves behind no trace, not even ash, like a burnt feather, or a beeswax candle.

Do animals live as if the final whistle might blow at any moment? Of course not; they don't even know that there is a final whistle. You know what it means but you choose to discount the knowledge, for obvious reasons.

The man falls head first, his legs and feet together, one long line of body. What you remember are the boots and his beauty.

The Earth falls silently through a vacuum. The man falls through air. He feels the air and hears the swoosh. His calm control is heartbreaking. Would you have twisted and shouted? You ask for miracles and then do not see them. A plane is absorbed into a building. On the screen there is no noise, no smells. Like pornography, scrubbed clean. And then it happens again. Another plane absorbed, slides into the building and does not re-emerge. Completely contained.

And so we live as if each moment is of no value because there are so many more to come, until at the last when only then does it truly begin to sink in that the moments that make up a life are numbered. Only when we become aware that the number of moments left to us will one day reach zero, only then do the moments take on value, increasing value as we hurry to the end, until two moments abut each other: a moment freighted with everything, and the moment that follows.

Or to end like this:

The squiggle Dickens made at the bottom of the page of the manuscript he abandoned right there, which would have to do instead of an ending, death insistent, hovering nearby.

I think of all those universes without both of us in them. And then I think of all those universes in which we never meet, all those universes in which you kill me, all those in which I kill you. Oh stop. You might as well believe in reincarnation as believe in the multiverse.

Have you noticed how petty you have become, how wrapped up in the trivial details of life? Did I turn off the gas? Did I unplug the toaster? I need to clean out the fridge. There are leaves that may or may not be blocking the drain outside the gate. Dust that no one will ever see unless they are standing on a chair is quietly and relentlessly piling up on top of the kitchen cupboards.

When you were young you were on the lookout against signs of encroaching pettiness and triviality, but it has come to you as it comes to everyone, no matter how much of an adventurer you might have been, or whether or not you once ran some large multinational company. Presidents and shopkeepers, it comes to you all in old age. Perhaps it is wisdom of a sort, the understanding that only the trivial really matters, that the trivial is what makes you most human, not the grand gestures of war but the small gesture that exists in making a cup of tea. Even the leaves that block the drain only got there because the Earth turned and autumn came around again.

A child had tugged at my coat. When was that? Was that the last time a human being had touched me? The child's mother had pulled her away and the little girl had turned back and looked straight at me. Our eyes met in some kind of understanding. What passed between us I cannot put into words, but something happened. No judgement. Simply, I was seen. God's gaze must be like that. Except that you can't look at God, can you? Not directly anyway. Perhaps it is different if God chooses to look at you. Perhaps then the look is not annihilating. Christ the vicar. The intermediary. To come in between. Little bird's feet. Prodding. Like wires. I feel them even through my thick coat. Like tiny electric shocks. The birds like me. By them at least, I am recognised. Beaked. Rail thin. Liminal. I am like a bird myself now. What a cliché. Old now but undimmed. Desire courses through my veins as if injected into me.

Sometimes I think my body is even more terrified of dying than I am. Sometimes in the night I wake with a start and it is the same old terror somewhere deep down, the same old nightmare dreamt for decades now.

The girl, I forget her name, though I liked her very much, later had an affair with the teacher. Was it later? Wasn't it after her mother had died? Her father, a charming, quiet and witty man, the local postman and the churchwarden, was never the same after his wife's death. He gave up being churchwarden, and then gave up coming to church at all. On his rounds now it looked as if the mail he carried had become an intolerable burden, an outward and visible sign of his grief at the death of his young wife. She must have been young, though I wouldn't have taken that in at the time when anyone over thirty was old, and everyone over forty indistinguishable. The mailbag that he had once carried lightly had become both a physical burden and the symbol of a burden. The mental and the physical had blurred. Perhaps mental burdens if they bear down long enough have the same physical effect as physical burdens; together make their mark on our bodies. I see him in my mind's eye, wearing his old age as if it were a coat he might fling off at any moment if he but had the strength.

Schubert wondered if there was anyone more wretched than he. Each night he went to bed praying that he would not wake up again to face another day. And yet, waking again to another day of wretchedness he began to write the 'Death and the Maiden' quartet. Ugly, diseased, in pain, he woke up and made art as beautiful and profound as any made by any human being ever.

Death presumably had encouraged a binary view of the world from the start: alive or dead. And then there was the question of sex: male or female? Religions, particularly their fundamentalist forms were strongly binary: right or wrong, saved or damned. Ironic then that religion should have adopted the intersex shaman as its intermediary between God and man.

The binary nature of life and death had fooled us into thinking that they were equal opposites, but what kind of opposition is it if the choice is between everything and nothing? Life overwhelms death because it is everything. Death overwhelms life because from the perspective of death life is the merest blip in eternity. Dead not just a long time, forever.

In the hospital bed she lies in a deep coma. Her daughter comes and plays her the music she loved in her youth and has loved all her life. Her daughter sings to her. Her mother's eyelids flutter, sometimes even open wide for a moment. Her daughter sees a smile playing on her mother's lips. The dying woman's husband disagrees. He reads the signs differently. Is she struggling? Is that anguish he detects?

He who was once so close to me and is now dead, I see as not dead but lost. It is the knowledge that he is helplessly lost that distresses me, that he is actually dead just numbs me. Death is not just far from the world of the living, there is a barrier between the two worlds that operates in only one direction. Like so many contingencies of the living world, death is beyond understanding. It is meaningless.

Even harder to make sense of: a before life and an after life.

Death cannot be like anything. Dying, however, is another matter.

They said you had only hours left to live. And so I sat at your bedside, my knees nearly touching the bag that was collecting your urine, waiting for the end to come, your end to come, your breaths more and more intermittent, as if the space between them was death itself coming in, you moving out from the shore, the tide reversed, broken waves made whole again, back to the swell, further out still to the ocean everywhere, horizon to horizon, dark and undifferentiated, back to what you had been before.

They said you had hours only left, but they were wrong. You did not die that day and the next day you were out of bed, sitting in a chair, furious that you were still here, desperate to have had done with it all, clear-minded, all there, plotting, gathering everything you had left in you in order to make a second assault. A different approach this time, in for the long haul. Days and days, and now they told me that it would likely be more days yet. I came not to visit so much as to look at you, to make sure you stayed submerged. You seemed to be hard at work at something, somewhere. Were you making progress? Several times a day I came and I looked and yet you appeared to me to be exactly the same as you had been the last time I looked, but what do I know?

Occasionally you would cough and I felt the entirety of you once more present in the room. I began to think you had fooled us all, not dying at all, merely protesting life. On the phone, they said you had gone, just like that, conscious, eyes open, one moment here, then not.

XIII

FRAGMENTS

(i) *It seems to me that as much history is in the 'insignificant' particulars, and that in a hundred years' time these very details will say more about the past than generalisations.*

(ii) *I don't enjoy travel for its own sake, but just for the people. I can't imagine travelling to see places. For the sake of half a dozen remarks, heard on the way to India – remarks which wouldn't have been made on any other trip – well it was worth going to India.*

(iii) *Grace Gregory, the former matron of Ambrose College, looked out of the plane window at the Alps below and, having found no apparent fault with them, returned her attention to her companion.*

(iv) *I have the idea of all and believe in all, / I believe materialism is true and spiritualism is true, I reject no part.*

(v) *One does not admire things enough: and worst of all one allows whole days to slip by without once pausing to see an object, any object, exactly as it is.*

(vi) *All the way to Heaven is Heaven.*

COMMENTARY

After years as a serialist composer, Arvo Pärt's discovery that a single note played beautifully is enough.

The comfort in old age that Darwin found in worms.

Lambent: moving about as if lightly touched.

Uncle Toby's search for a perfect and truthful account of the battle of Namur that drowns him in a study of everything.

The chord of E flat major out of which a world is woven, and which in the minor – many hours later – signals its destruction.

Your love of fireworks. The most democratic of all art forms, you tell people. No reductive explanation gets close. Colourful, playful, exuberant. All energy and form. Over in a moment, and then everywhere as clouds of ash descending gently.

Mallemaroking: the carousing of seamen on icebound ships.

One can be mistaken in the details, if not also in everything.

The exacted promise from which Wotan never recovers. See also King Lear and Rama's father.

We're here because we're here because we're here.

Lord Byron in a gondola on the Grand Canal nibbling at polenta that is being kept warm between the breasts of a lover.

One hundred and eight billion, the number of human beings that has ever lived, someone once calculated.

Apocatastasis: the restitution of all things to their original state.

My life is a story that interests me greatly, wrote Berlioz in his memoirs.

It is not necessarily egotistical, he said, to insist on an 'I'; it invites the other to join in, even if it is to reject you. Better than the adamant 'we' that offers no choice.

Julianus Didius's purchase of the Roman Empire from the praetorian guard.

She said to me, experiments put the world into a straitjacket. This is not how the world is, but how the world can be made to be. When do you ever live under laboratory conditions? When in life are you ever under exam conditions? Except of course when you are actually the subject of an experiment, or taking an exam.

On a fault line, after atom bombs had wiped out two of its cities, still Japan chose atomic power.

The Oracle or Google? Discuss.

Bruckner's dedication of his ninth symphony to 'the dear Lord'. *If I die before it is finished, God will have only Himself to blame.* He dies, the symphony unfinished.

You dream that you have arrived at infinity. Everywhere there are typewriters and monkeys. All around you radiation, enfeebled by its long journey, falls exhausted into nothing at all. Parallel lines meet up with a barely audible tinkling sound, and infinite sequences of numbers plop gently into their final definite sums. You see clouds of deltas condensing into tiny, hard little differential 'd's. You bow to the largest prime. You can just make out the last digit of pi, it is a three, or, wait, is it a . . . ?

At a lunch party thrown by Harpo Marx for Beatrice Lillie, Fanny Brice and Arnold Schoenberg, Fanny Brice asks Schoenberg what hits he has written, and perhaps because of his reluctance to elaborate, repeatedly says, 'C'mon, Professor, play us a tune'.

On to the next stage! Forwards with physics!

Agelast: one who never laughs.

Using long tapers, the almost simultaneous lighting of some one thousand lamps at Vauxhall Gardens, then one of London's greatest attractions.

You believe that you can transcend the universe itself. You never do of course, but believing that you can has taken you somewhere.

They swooped down and started dropping incendiary bombs. You heard the sound of the planes. Seconds later the pretty village was a mass of flames. You were ten years old. I have seen nothing like it since, you said. No one knew where to run to, but everyone was running, some with their clothes on fire, hair on fire; cats, dogs, cows all running too. A single air raid in a single village. A thousand dead.

Look into a mirror every day, remind yourself of your beauty and your youth, Aristotle encouraged the young.

$e^{i\pi} + 1 = 0$. The exponential, the imaginary, the circle and numbers, combined together in a certain way nothing at all.

An indulgence bought from Pope Hadrian, good for 1,902,202 years and 202 days release from the sufferings of purgatory.

Not by accident nor by design, each as ludicrous an idea as the other.

Leonardo aged thirty said he could do anything in painting that it was possible to do. Perhaps, but there were lots of things he might have done that he didn't think of doing. We had to wait for Cy Twombly.

Is this how you know how much you love him, that you would give up anything and everything just to see him again for one more second, to be able to touch him just one more time?

Audiences packed the Alhambra Music Hall in Leicester Square to see *Cheese Mites*, a minute-long silent film made by an amateur naturalist who had placed a camera on top of a microscope.

Those people willing to take a one-way trip to some far-flung planet, and in order to see what: some bigger mountain, maybe a double sunset? To trade life for that!

Work in Progress, what James Joyce first calls *Finnegans Wake*.

Not a door, not even a threshold to a door.

Once, just before my own birthday party, my mother said, Try not to draw attention to yourself.

On 24 June 1645, the king's protectors complain that they would never have surrendered the besieged city of Oxford if the ladies of the court there had not demanded fresh butter for their early peas.

Perhaps just accept that you got here somehow and leave it at that.

Emily Dickinson making gingerbread, Virginia Woolf cottage loaves and marmalade.

The aching love I have for you that feels akin to nausea.

How can you not believe in progress?

Debussy as a young man taught Madame von Meck's children to play the piano. His imitation of Massenet had the household in hysterics.

Stalin had his poets arrested randomly and for no reason. Not just poets of course. He was at least in this democratic.

The inward turn toward the self that apparently occurred somewhere between AD 100 and 200.

The earthquake in Lisbon that precipitated the age of enlightenment.

His stepdaughter came to him on his deathbed to tell him that there was no more money. 'Oh dear,' he said, 'I thought there would be enough for another fortnight.'

Oneness. Wholeness. Holiness. The void that is the origin of the world of physics. Time. Eternity. Infinity. The infinitesimal. These and other such mysteries.

Don't be a clever clogs. Too clever by half. Grow up. Cheer up. Just be yourself. What are you doing inside on a day like today? Did they like you?

Catoptromancy: divination by means of a mirror.

There wasn't much to see, said Buzz Aldrin.

The so-called honeycomb conjecture proven in 1999, that bees seem to have known all along.

She said to you, the world is a mirror of your emotions. But I know myself least of all, you said. It is hardly surprising, then, that I do not see myself reflected there.

Pepys arranging his books in order of size.

It's all very well saying that motion is only relative, but it feels real enough when you are on a plane crossing the ocean and I am left here alone.

Samuel George Morton, a physician from Philadelphia, and his collection of some one thousand human skulls.

The mood of a dream, even a dream forgotten, that colours the whole of the next day; the logic of waking life turning what had made dream-sense into nonsense; the fragments of the dream dissolving into nothing, and yet the essence of the thing, the feeling remaining.

Brunelleschi's discovery of linear perspective.

Doesn't matter. Fudged. Best we can do.

Why all the fuss about getting to the top of things?

The moment in Bruckner's Fifth Symphony when the notes fall like tender rain.

That no matter how long you live, it will have been only the one life.

Elizabeth I's disapproval of the flushing lavatory and her refusal to use one.

How many times have you looked up the word hermeneutics? How many times have you forgotten what it means?

What a piece of work is man!

Byron listening to Herschel's account of a vivisection then staying on to protest the cruelty.

That infinity *minus* infinity has no answer, but infinity *plus* infinity is infinity.

Whatever it is that you recollect of the past and conjure up in imagination – whether life that is seconds gone or long gone – is remembered only from some particular vantage point. If everything is not to collapse into meaningless relativism you must choose some perspective, a point of view. Close up, you see only the details and not the undercurrents, from far enough away you might see almost anything.

World-line, the history of an object through space-time.

It was the third time that she had failed to recognise me. 'It's nothing personal,' she said. 'These days, I just don't remember nouns.'

The view from the base of the mountain might well be as fine as the view from the summit. Finer even.

In dreams, no progress nor processes.

At the next table the American complaining that his Bonsai trees are too small.

Einstein said that the only reason he turned up at his office in Princeton was so that he could walk home with Gödel.

Dromophobia: fear of crossing the road.

At 9.51 p.m. on Tuesday, 13 February 1945 the carpet bombing began. No one knows how many died. Perhaps 25,000; perhaps 135,000.

The last person to hold the post of Master of the Revels.

It is because we cling to life that we cannot make the dance leap into death, so says Kierkegaard.

The summit is for heroes, hermits and other misfits.

Your failure to get your ego and body to agree with each other.

By the end of the war, the Jewish population of Europe had been reduced from around nine million to around three million.

You don't remember now what it was that Jung wrote about an important dream he had had; what you remember is that he wakes up his wife so that she can check the time and write it up in a notebook kept by their bedside for the purpose. It is three in the morning.

Your conflation of the material world with the real world (whatever that is).

Webern accidentally shot and killed by a confused military cook who drinks himself to death out of feelings of guilt.

The inward experience of not being here, which is why you prefer sleep.

The mild stir her presence caused in Wiesbaden in 1850.

Who is it that I am?

He believes that the physical world is everything. He concludes that he might as well decide everything himself. One of the many roads that leads to the gas chambers.

Your friend laughs when you tell her that your cashmere has been ruined by moths. You can see her point. You feel hurt nevertheless.

Who gets to decide? The masses? An elite? Scientists?

As a boy, Albert Camus saw his grandmother cut off the head of a chicken, an experience, he said, from which he never recovered; the image still vivid when he wrote a paper that brought about the end of capital punishment in France.

Chickens not so fortunate.

Not only competition, cooperation.

Abelard and Heloise's son Astrolabe. I wonder what became of him?

No one knows how many people died during Stalin's reign. It is generally agreed that it is at least twenty million, some say as many as forty million or even fifty million; if the latter figure then one in three of the population.

If you had free will, what would you be free from? You cannot escape the laws of nature. There is no crevice to crawl into that separates you from the world. You do not have free will but you have the illusion of it, which will serve you just as well.

In the opening pages of *Walden*, Thoreau berates humankind for its foolhardiness, its lack of courage, and its failure to try the new and to test the boundaries of what it might be to be a human being.

She says to you, so now you are blaming the universe.

To the clown everything is always new.

Free won't.

Emily Davison steps out in front of the king's horse and is trampled to death. When they search her pockets they find a return train ticket.

Perhaps even more in Maoist China.

Scriabin instructed that it be performed in the Himalayas with bells hanging from clouds.

What if this is as good as it gets. Not just in my lifetime, I mean what if this is as good as it is ever going to get in the whole history of the universe.

You do it for your tribe, for friends, for unknown friends, unknown tribesmen.

I think I may be lost.

No Native Americans, no Jews, no meadows, no cups of tea.

You try to work out how to chart a course between nihilism and sentimentality.

When asked why, aged ninety-three, he still practised the cello for three hours every day, Pablo Casals said that he had begun to notice some improvement.

A clue: all kinds of life developed right here at home.

She says, Can you afford not to?

You said to me that only Keats could have written 'Ode to a Nightingale' and that someone else would have discovered Uranus eventually. But perhaps the universe isn't like that; perhaps everything really would have turned out differently if it had been someone other than Herschel.

We all die in the end, which is a crumb of comfort.

Mendelssohn of music: a language too precise for words.

You have always thought that there is something fishy about the concept of physical inertia.

Thankful villages, those villages in which no one was lost during the war.

In a letter, Lampedusa wrote that the key to understanding *The Leopard* is to be found in the character of the dog Bendicò.

You live as if there is a core you that is the real you and might be removed and transplanted elsewhere, if you knew but how.

In July 1937 a cartoon appeared in *Punch* that divided the country: two hippopotamuses in a swamp in the middle of nowhere; their heads just lifted out of the mud. One says to the other, 'I keep thinking it's Thursday.'

Perhaps what is truly terrifying is not how large the universe is, but how small.

Not only violence, kindness.

He is ready now to give up the idea of the particle. The foundations of his world instantly disappear.

The emperor orders his men to destroy the town of Weisberg and its besieged inhabitants. The women are to be spared. They may take with them whatever possessions they can carry on their shoulders. The women emerge, their possessions left behind, each staggering under the weight of a husband. The emperor spares everyone.

Trust the Christians to call it the Greatest Story Ever Told.

It ought to be clear where you fit in but when you try nothing comes into focus, or everything does. You are tossed about between everything and nothing, arrogance and false modesty. You have come to the conclusion that from your perspective there is nothing other than the menacing sense that almost everything lurks behind what you do see.

Messiaen's *Quartet for the End of Time* had its first performance outside in front of an audience of five thousand prisoners of war. The cello only had three strings and the piano was out of tune. So said Messiaen. In his nineties, the cellist said that the conditions of the performance had indeed been difficult but that Messiaen had exaggerated. The performance took place indoors and the audience could have numbered no more than three hundred.

As I say, I confess at once how little I am touched by the desire for accuracy.

You no longer belong to a single tribe; you belong to many tribes that overlap. Countless numbers of tribes. The illusion of your individuality is precisely the unique map of the overlapping tribes to which you belong.

Jewish injunction: Repair the World.

I do not see the one thing about me that is the key to my unhappiness. It may well be plain to others but I do not see it.

Louis XVI at Versailles mending locks when the revolution arrives.

Cheer me / cashmere me.

If it weren't for Stalin, Shostakovich would almost certainly be more famous as an opera composer than as a symphonist. I think of all those who lost their lives during those years. None of them known to me, and so many! I do not feel anything. I think of all those lost operas.

What is left when you have said no to everything that you dare say no to? How far down into the murk are you prepared to go? Further down than you wanted to go? So far down that, being too scared to say no, you face the possibility of having to say yes? Is what you finally say yes to what you get to last of all?

E. M. Forster writes in his locked diary what he could not say in person: 'I love you, Syed Ross Masood: love.'

Not only fragmentation, concord.

Mahler, in tears, leaning out of his bedroom window, the funeral procession of a fireman passing by. The thwack every so often of the drum in his last and unfinished symphony.

Maybe is more often the answer.

Not hilarity, a substance soon exhausted, but hilaritas, the state of being happy for no apparent reason at all, the opposite of depression.

Throughout all human history somewhere between 150 million and a billion.

Now they tell us that the particles didn't bang into each other after all, they came together slowly over time.

Sometimes relativism is of no account; there is only the right thing to do, regardless of logic.

I regret the loss of what might have been, but the loss is all part of it.

On the train, on the tracks that stretch to infinity.

The prisoner seen every day evidently happy, perhaps even on the day the doors close behind him.

In the days and hours of his final illness his dog refused to come near him. Now, she jumps onto the bed and lies alongside his body.

I couldn't make it all right for you. I wanted to but I couldn't. At least I know now how much I loved you, which is something.

Life matters. Nothing else.

SOURCES

The Waste Land, T. S. Eliot.

I
(i) *The Sword in the Stone*, T. H. White. Written on a sign above an ant colony.
(ii) *Daniel Deronda*, George Eliot.
(iii) *Happy Days*, Samuel Beckett.
(iv) 'De Profundis', Oscar Wilde.

II
(i) Michael Frayn.

III
(i) *The Bachelors*, Muriel Spark.
(ii) *Riders in the Chariot*, Patrick White.

IV
(i) *Parade's End*, Ford Madox Ford.
(ii) *A Last Diary (1921)*, W. N. P. Barbellion.
(iii) Brigid Brophy.
(iv) 'The Affliction (I)', George Herbert.
(v) Matthew Burgess.

V
(i) John Keats, in a letter.
(ii) 'Unspeakable', *Stag's Leap*, Sharon Olds.
(iii) *Middlemarch*, George Eliot.
(iv) Source lost.
(v) Sigmund Freud.
(vi) *Villette*, Charlotte Brontë.

(vii) Harry Levin, in his introduction to *The Ambassadors* by Henry James.

VI
(i) *Walden*, Henry Thoreau.

VII
(i) *To Noto*, Duncan Fallowell.
(ii) *Paradise Lost*, John Milton.
(iii) Sam Wollaston, in the *Guardian*, 13 March 2014.

VIII
(i) *The Dyer's Hand*, W. H. Auden.
(ii) *Remembrance of Things Past*, Marcel Proust.
(iii) *A Passage to India*, E. M. Forster.
(iv) *The Transit of Venus*, Shirley Hazzard.
(v) 'De Profundis', Oscar Wilde.
(vi) *The Varieties of Religious Experience*, William James.
(vii) *Augustus*, John Williams.
(viii) Vincent van Gogh, in a letter to his brother Theo.

IX
(i) Montagu Slater, in his libretto to Benjamin Britten's *Peter Grimes*.
(ii) John Keats, in a letter.
(iii) Diane Arbus.
(iv) *Confessions of Felix Krull*, Thomas Mann.

X

(i) *Down with Skool!,* Geoffrey Willans.
(ii) *The Transit of Venus,* Shirley Hazzard.
(iii) Source lost.
(iv) Simone Weil.
(v) *Among Men and Beasts,* Paul Trepman.

XI

(i) *Middlemarch,* George Eliot.
(ii) *Middlemarch,* George Eliot.
(iii) *Tristram Shandy,* Laurence Sterne.
(iv) 'Divinity', George Herbert.
(v) Rolf Fjelde, from his introduction to
    Four Major Plays by Henrik Ibsen.
(vi) *Some Metaphysical Problems
    Pragmatically Considered,* William
    James.
(vii) *The Prelude,* William Wordsworth.

XII

(i) *The Age of Innocence,* Edith Wharton.
(ii) Henry Wadsworth Longfellow.
(iii) *Jude the Obscure,* Thomas Hardy.
(iv) *Early One Morning,* Walter de la
    Mare.
(v) *A Last Diary,* W. N. P. Barbellion.

XIII

(i) *Becoming a Londoner,* David Plante.
(ii) *The Signpost,* E. Arnot Robertson.
(iii) *Territorial Rights,* Muriel Spark.
(iv) 'Leaves of Grass', Walt Whitman.
(v) *Mr Fortune's Maggot,* Sylvia
    Townsend Warner.
(vi) St Catherine of Siena.